AN ANNOTATED LIST OF THE BIRDS OF BOLIVIA

AN ANNOTATED LIST OF THE BIRDS OF BOLIVIA

J. V. REMSEN, JR.* & MELVIN A. TRAYLOR, JR.**

*Museum of Natural Science, Louisiana State University,
Baton Rouge, Louisiana 70803
**Division of Birds, Field Museum of Natural History,
Roosevelt Rd. at Lake Shore Dr., Chicago, Illinois 60605

Cover painting of an adult Red-fronted Macaw
from a mixed media painting by John P. O'Neill

BUTEO BOOKS
Vermillion, South Dakota

First published in USA in 1989 by Buteo Books,
PO Box 481, Vermillion, South Dakota 57069.

Library of Congress Catalog Card Number 89-061415
ISBN 0-931130-16-6

Printed in the United States of America by
Intercollegiate Press, Shawnee Mission, Kansas

CONTENTS

TABLES

Table 1. Species (N=80) recorded from lowland southeastern
    Peru and southwestern Brazil that have not been
    recorded in Bolivia. 12
Table 2. Number of bird species in the "life zones" of Bolivia. 15
Table 3. Most frequent "life zone" distribution patterns for bird
    species in Bolivia, with percent of total number of species
    known from Bolivia for each pattern. 16

FIGURE

Figure 1. Map of Departamentos and Habitats of Bolivia. 6

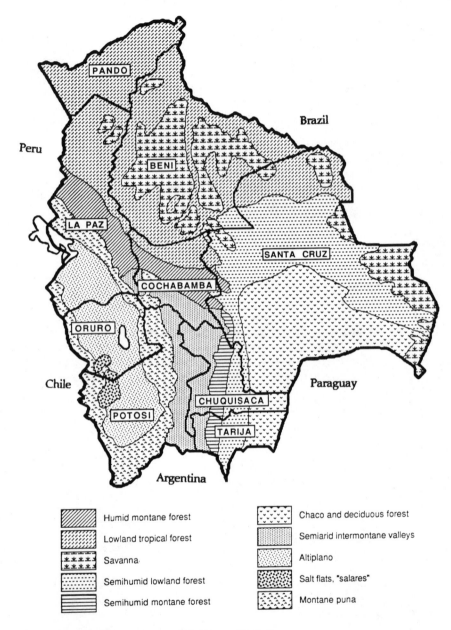

Legend:

- ▨ Humid montane forest
- ▨ Lowland tropical forest
- ✳ Savanna
- ⋯ Semihumid lowland forest
- ▤ Semihumid montane forest
- ⋯ Chaco and deciduous forest
- ▦ Semiarid intermontane valleys
- ⬚ Altiplano
- ▨ Salt flats, "salares"
- ∿ Montane puna

Figure 1. Map of Departamentos and Habitats of Bolivia.

INTRODUCTION

Bolivia has one of the richest avifaunas of any country in the world. Although completely land-locked and therefore lacking any marine littoral or pelagic bird species, Bolivia's total of 1274 species places it among the countries with the most diversity in the world, with over 40% of the birds of South America found within its boundaries; the avifauna of Bolivia is certainly the largest of any land-locked country in the world. Because many critical regions within Bolivia's boundaries have yet to be surveyed by ornithologists, it is likely that at least another 150 or so species will eventually be added to the list.

Why does Bolivia have so many species of birds? Bolivia's tremendous topographic diversity and its location at tropical latitudes combine to produce a great variety of habitats, each with its characteristic species assemblage. Habitats range from lowland Amazonian rainforest to perpetually snow-covered mountaintops (see Fig. 1).

At its northern boundary, Bolivia's lowland rainforests are among the richest in the world. These forests, with an avifauna typical of Amazonian habitats, extend unbroken through the lowlands of Departamentos La Paz and Pando to northern Dpto. Beni and in tongues of suitable habitat southward along the Río Guaporé on the Brazilian border, the Río Mamoré in central Beni, and along the base of the Andes from Dpto. Cochabamba to Prov. Ichilo, Dpto. Santa Cruz. In the latter region, approximately 150 species characteristic of Amazonian habitats reach their southern limit (Remsen, Traylor, and Parkes 1987).

In northern Dpto. Beni, patches of "pampas" grassland and savanna appear as islands in the Amazonian forest, and proceeding south, the pampas soon form a greater proportion of the total habitat until forest becomes restricted mainly to river edges ("gallery forest"). Birds of the "pampas" region are typical of those of the wet *pantanal* habitat of Mato Grosso, Brazil, with species of Amazonian riverine habitats in the gallery forests (Remsen 1986). Many *pantanal* species are also found along the Brazilian border in extreme eastern Dpto. Santa Cruz. The permanent marshes and the seasonally flooded grasslands of these regions provide habitat for huge populations of waterbirds.

Farther south, in Dpto. Santa Cruz, deciduous forests appear that continue all the way to the Argentina-Paraguay border; in the extreme south, these forests become dry and are continuous with the *Chaco* of western Paraguay and northwestern Argentina. In these areas, birds characteristic of the subtropical lowlands of southern South America predominate, and as the border with Paraguay is reached, the avifauna is typical of that of the Chaco (Short 1975). Within this general region are found scattered patches of "cerrado" (low, scrubby open woodland with tall grass understory) that support species typical of western Brazil.

In the Andes, cloudforest extends along the eastern slope from the Peruvian border to Dpto. Cochabamba, and patches of depauperate cloudforest can be found farther south, from Dpto. Santa Cruz through dptos. Chuquisaca and Tarija to the border with Argentina. Birds typical of humid Andean cloudforest are found along this eastern slope of the Andes through Dpto. La Paz to Dpto. Cochabamba. Although a few species (20) apparently do not cross the dry canyon of the upper Río Beni-Río La Paz, this cloudforest avifauna is largely intact as far south as Prov. Chapare, Dpto. Cochabamba. At least 110 species of the humid eastern slope reach their southern limit in Dpto. Cochabamba, mostly in Prov. Chapare. Another 70 cloudforest species extend as far south as various localities in Dpto. Santa Cruz (Remsen, Traylor, and Parkes 1987); only a few species of humid forest

7

occur farther south than Prov. Caballero, Dpto. Santa Cruz. Although the cloudforest region of southern Bolivia in Dptos. Chuquisaca and Tarija is depauperate, it contains several species endemic to the humid eastern slopes of the Andes from Chuquisaca to northern Argentina (*Penelope dabbenei, Amazona tucumana, Eriocnemis glaucopoides, Veniliornis frontalis, Scytalopus superciliaris,* and *Cinclus schulzi*).

The drier intermontane valleys of the eastern Andes from Dpto. La Paz to northern Argentina, with their brushy, xeromorphic vegetation, overlap very little in species composition with the cloudforest avifauna of the nearby rain-drenched, more eastern-facing, forested slopes. These dry valleys are rich in endemic species: *Ara rubrogenys, Sappho sparganura, Oreotrochilus adela, Geositta rufipennis, Upucerthia andaecola, Upucerthia harterti, Mimus dorsalis, Oreopsar bolivianus, Poospiza boliviana, P. hypochondriaca,* and *Sicalis luteocephala*. Many of these species reach their northern limit just south of the city of La Paz at Huajchilla, Prov. Murillo (E. Flores and Remsen, unpubl. data).

Birds of elevations above timberline in the Andes are characteristic of the *puna* avifauna that extends from Argentina to northern Peru. See Vuilleumier and Simberloff (1980) and Fjeldså (1985) for general zoogeography of these high elevation species.

In addition to the resident avifauna, Bolivia receives numbers of migrant species that winter there. Although most are austral migrants (from southern South America), 45 species of migrants from North America (indicated by "(N)" in the Main List), of which 19 are shorebirds and 18 are passerines, also reach Bolivia. Unfortunately, our knowledge of seasonal movements of birds within South America and within Bolivia is at a primitive stage. At present, we can not even be sure whether certain species breed in Bolivia or are present only as austral or intratropical migrants. We predict that many species, particularly waterbirds, now assumed to be permanent will be found to be dramatically seasonal in their presence in Bolivia as a whole or its component regions.

Sixteen species of birds are endemic to Bolivia, and most are rare with small geographic ranges. One of these, the Coppery Thorntail (*Popelairia letitiae*) is apparently still known only from two males without locality data that presumably came from northeastern Bolivia; it hasn't been seen or collected in this century. Two other endemics are found in the lowlands of dptos. Beni and Santa Cruz: the Blue-throated Macaw (*Ara glaucogularis,* formerly *A. caninde*) and the Unicolored Thrush (*Turdus haplochrous*). The macaw, long thought to be a subspecies or color morph of the widespread Blue-and-yellow Macaw (*A. ararauna*), is known from only five museum specimens, two of which lack locality data (Ingels, Parkes, and Farrand 1981). This spectacular bird is currently exported illegally in small numbers by parrot dealers in Santa Cruz. Nothing is known of its natural history or population status. The Unicolored Thrush is known only from about six specimens and is perhaps the rarest extant New World thrush.

Three other endemics, the Bolivian Recurvebill (*Simoxenops striatus*), the Yungas Tody-Tyrant (*Hemitriccus spodiops*), and the Ashy Antwren (*Myrmotherula grisea*), share similar distributions along the base of the eastern Andes in northern Bolivia. Nothing is known of the recurvebill beyond the locality data from fewer than 10 specimens. The scanty information known for the Ashy Antwren, known from only 12 specimens, and the Yungas Tody-Tyrant, known from only 16 specimens, is summarized by Remsen, Parker, and Ridgely (1982). Rapid clearing of forests along the base of the Andes threatens the existence of all three, although the tody-tyrant, found in disturbed second growth at forest edges, may benefit from partial clearing.

The remaining endemics are found in the Andes proper. The Rufous-faced Antpitta (*Grallaria erythrotis*) and the Black-throated Spinetail (*Schizoeaca harterti*) are common birds in upper elevation cloudforest in northern Bolivia (see Remsen, Parker, and Ridgely (1982) and Remsen (1981), respectively, for natural history). The Black-hooded Sunbeam (*Aglaeactis pamela*), a striking hummingbird known from only a handful of localities, is found only on brushy slopes of the eastern Andes in semihumid valleys above timberline. Berlepsch's Canastero (*Asthenes berlepschi*) is known only from a few localities at high elevations of the Eastern Cordillera in Dpto. La Paz; nothing has been published concerning its natural history.

Six endemics are found in brushy habitats in the dry intermontane valleys of the central Bolivian Andes: the Red-fronted Macaw (*Ara rubrogenys*), the Wedge-tailed Hillstar (*Oreotrochilus adela*), the Bolivian Earthcreeper (*Upucerthia harterti*), the Bolivian Warbling-Finch (*Poospiza boliviana*), the Citron-headed Yellow-Finch (*Sicalis luteocephala*), and the Bolivian Blackbird (*Oreopsar bolivianus*). Natural history information for the macaw is summarized by Ridgely (1981). This species, one of the most beautiful parrots in the New World, has a very small distribution in Dptos. Cochabamba and Santa Cruz, and in view of its exploitation by parrot dealers and its official declaration as a pest species (because it attacks peanut and corn plantations), its population status needs to be determined; Ridgely (1981) estimated that the total population does not exceed 3,000 individuals. Natural history information for the Bolivian Earthcreeper is summarized by Remsen, Schmitt, and Schmitt (in press) and for the Bolivian Blackbird, by Orians *et al.* (1977). Nothing has been published concerning the other three. The final endemic, the Cochabamba Mountain-Finch (*Poospiza (Compsospiza) garleppi*), has one of the most restricted distributions of any South American bird; it is known from only 9 localities at upper elevations in southern Dpto. Cochabamba (Remsen, Schmitt, and Schmitt, in press).

At the time of publication of Meyer de Schauensee (1966), five other species were considered endemic to Bolivia. The Rufous-bellied Saltator (*Saltator rufiventris*), although still known within Bolivia only from the same small area as the Cochabamba Mountain-Finch, has now been found in extreme northern Argentina in Jujuy (Olrog and Contino 1970). The Gray-crowned Tyrannulet (*Serpophaga griseiceps* Berlioz) was determined by Traylor (1982) to be a specimen in juvenal plumage of the White-bellied Tyrannulet (*S. munda*). The Santa Cruz Siskin (*Carduelis santaecrucis*) is now considered a subspecies of the Hooded Siskin (*Carduelis magellanica*; Howell, Paynter, and Rand 1968). The Light-crowned Spinetail (*Cranioleuca albiceps*) was recently found in extreme southern Peru (Remsen 1984), as was the Scimitar-winged Piha, *Lipaugus uropygialis* (T. S. Schulenberg and L. C. Binford, unpubl. data).

Bolivia is one of the least-studied countries of South America, especially considering that its avifauna is one of the richest. For example, the ornithological gazetteer for Bolivia (Paynter, Traylor, and Winter 1975) contains only 71 pages of collecting localities; this contrasts dramatically with Peru, which, with an area only 16% larger than that of Bolivia, has a gazetteer (Stephens and Traylor 1983) with 241 pages of localities, or 239% more than that of Bolivia. Ecuador, with only 26% as much area as Bolivia, has a gazetteer (Paynter and Traylor 1977) with 137 pages, nearly twice as many as that of Bolivia.

No summary of Bolivian birds has appeared since Bond and Meyer de Schauensee's (1942-43) annotated list. In the ensuing 45 years, knowledge of bird distribution in Bolivia has increased substantially, primarily through the efforts of the Steinbachs (see Remsen, Traylor, and Parkes 1985, 1986, and 1987), the Ollala expeditions in northern Bolivia (Gyldenstolpe 1945a, Fjeldså 1987), G. Niethammer (1953, 1956), Claes Olrog (1949, 1963), and recent collections by K. Stager and S. C. Bromley for the Los Angeles County Museum, by Richard Crossin and Roy Steinbach for the Field Museum of Natural History,

10

J. Cabot and P. Serrano for the Estación Biologica Doñana, and by Remsen, C. Gregory Schmitt, Donna C. Schmitt, Manuel Sánchez S., Linda S. Hale, T. A. Parker III, Steven W. Cardiff, Angelo P. Capparella, Scott M. Lanyon, Thomas S. Schulenberg, David Wiedenfeld, Carlos E. Quintela, John A. Gerwin, Kenneth V. Rosenberg, Eliana I. Flores, John M. Bates, Mary C. Garvin, and others for the Museum of Natural Science, Louisiana State University (see bibliography). Bond and Meyer de Schauensee (1942, 1943) reported 1,909 species-department records representing 940 currently recognized species; we here report an additional 2,651 records, an increase in distribution data on a departmental basis of 139%, and an additional 333 species, an increase of 35%. The papers that have added the greatest number of departmental records since Bond and Meyer de Schauensee (1942, 1943) have been: (1) Gyldenstolpe (1945) with 560 additions; (2) the series by Remsen, Traylor, and Parkes (1985, 1986, and 1987) with 393 additions; (3) Remsen, Parker, Quintela, and Rosenberg (MS) with 161 additions; (4) Niethammer (1953, 1956) with 156 additions, and (5) Laubmann (1930) with 87 additions.

The area in greatest need of exploration in Bolivia is its northern, Amazonian region in Dpto. Pando and in northern Dpto. La Paz in Prov. Iturralde. Only two localities in Pando have been sampled: Victoria, on the extreme southern border of Pando and very near relatively well-known localities in Dpto. Beni (Gyldenstolpe 1945) and the Cobija area (Parker and Remsen 1987; Remsen, Parker, Quintela, and Rosenberg, MS). Other than T. A. Parker's brief but productive survey along the Río Heath (Parker, MS), the Amazonian sections of Dpto. La Paz have yet to be sampled. The bird species recorded at four areas in extreme southeastern Peru and southwestern Brazil within 60 to 225 km of the Bolivian border include 80 species not yet recorded from Bolivia (Table 1). Elsewhere in Amazonia, recent fieldwork in extreme northeastern Prov. Velasco, Dpto. Santa Cruz (Bates et al., in press) has revealed that many species previously thought not to occur west of the Madeira-Guaporé drainage cross the upper Guaporé, and future field work may reveal that many more species from Rondonia, Brazil, may occur in this area of Bolivia (Table 1).

Another area in need of exploration is the humid slope of the eastern Andes north of the Río Mapiri canyon in Prov. Iturralde, Dpto. La Paz; the LSUMZ collection contains specimens of 13 species, as yet unrecorded in Bolivia, known from within about 35 km of the Bolivian border in extreme southern Dpto. Puno, Peru: *Nothoprocta taczanowskii, Cypseloides cryptus, Eriocnemis luciani, Schizoeaca helleri, Premnornis guttuligera, Chloropipo unicolor, Phyllomyias cinereiceps, Phylloscartes poecilotis, Cyphorhinus thoracicus, Atlapetes brunneinucha, Iridosornis analis, Tangara viridicollis,* and the newly discovered *T. meyerdeschauensei* (see Schulenberg and Binford 1985). Other poorly known areas of Bolivia likely to yield new records for Bolivia include the entire Bolivian portion of the Cordillera Occidental of the Andes, the provinces of Mamoré and Itenez in Dpto. Beni, the province of Sandoval in extreme northeastern Dpto. Santa Cruz, and the Bañados de Izozog and surrounding area in southern Dpto. Santa Cruz. Although these areas will probably yield the highest number of surprises, almost any area in the country can produce important records. For example, in 1980 the first records of the Sickle-winged Guan (*Chamaepetes goudotii*) for Bolivia were obtained within two hours of Bolivia's largest city, La Paz, and 50 meters from one of the busiest roads in the country (Cardiff and Remsen 1981).

If Bolivia had not lost so much of its territory to neighboring countries in various wars over the last century, its current boundaries would include the Pacific Coast as far south as Antofagasta, much of extreme southeastern Peru, portions of southwestern Brazil (Acre and Mato Grosso), the northwestern half of Paraguay, and portions of northern

Argentina. These lost territories probably contain 100-200 species not known from the modern boundaries of Bolivia.

The purpose of this checklist is to provide a complete list of species recorded in Bolivia and for each of its nine departamentos. For a species' occurrence in each departamento, we provide a literature citation, a feature that is probably unique for any Neotropical checklist. The numbers in the Main List refer to the number of the citation in the Literature Cited that reported the first specimen for that Departamento. However, if Bond and Meyer de Schauensee (1942, 1943) reported a locality record for a Departamento, we usually cite them, because of the seminal nature of their publication, even if a record had been published earlier for that Departamento. Citations in the Literature Cited without cross-reference numbers are those mentioned in the Introduction, Taxonomic Footnotes, or Hypothetical List that do not appear in the checklist itself. If a specimen record has been published subsequent to a published sight record, we cite the specimen record, not the sight record. References that do not give a locality for the reported specimen are placed in parentheses (and should be treated with caution). Previously published departmental records that we are certain are erroneous have been deleted altogether; for example, the Carriker collecting locality "Mouth of the Rio Chapare" is often considered to be in Dpto. Beni, but is actually in Dpto. Cochabamba. The specimen records from unpublished manuscripts in the literature cited are all deposited at the Museum of Natural Science, Louisiana State University. Records supported by published photographs, photographs on file at VIREO (Academy of Natural Sciences of Philadelphia), or sound recordings (mainly by T. A. Parker, III) deposited at the Library of Natural Sounds, Laboratory of Ornithology, Cornell University, are noted with a double dagger ($\ddagger$). Sight records are noted with an asterisk (*); of the 1272 species in the main checklist, and the two introduced species, the inclusion of only 22 (1.7%) is based on sight records only. We have not included certain published sight records for which we feel that specimen documentation is necessary, and we encourage users of the checklist to treat all sight records with caution.

We follow the taxonomy of Morony, Bock, and Farrand (1975) except for those families covered by the three Peters' Check-list volumes (Museum of Comparative Zoology) that have appeared since Morony, Bock, and Farrand (1975). We have also incorporated changes that have appeared in the AOU Check-list (1983), as well as some others that have appeared in recent literature; footnotes alert the reader to most of these changes and the appropriate literature. We recognize that advances in biochemical systematics will doubtless revolutionize the arrangement and sequence of higher taxa (e.g., Sibley, Ahlquist, and Monroe 1988); nevertheless, we retain a more traditional sequence of taxa in this list (with some exceptions, such as storks and vultures), because many of the proposed changes are controversial. For English names, we follow Meyer de Schauensee (1970). Although in some cases "better" English names could be devised, we have resisted the temptation to meddle with established names, most of which have been in use for more than 20 years (i.e., since Meyer de Schauensee 1966); many are even older.

The last column of the checklist contains a code for various "life zones" in which each species occurs (excluding unusual records of wandering individuals). These life zone designations should be regarded as preliminary, especially for many species of the southwestern quartile of the country, where the authors have had no first-hand experience. It must be emphasized that the designations apply to their distribution as currently known within Bolivia and therefore do not include our information from other

Table 1. Species (N = 80) recorded from five localities* in lowland southeastern Peru and southwestern Brazil that have not been recorded in Bolivia.

Species	Tpta	Manu	Balta	Purús	Rond
Botaurus pinnatus Pinnated Bittern	X				
Nothocrax urumutum Nocturnal Curassow					X
Psophia viridis Dark-winged Trumpeter					X
Aramides calopterus Red-winged Wood-Rail			X		
Laterallus fasciatus Black-banded Crake			X		
Brotogeris chrysopterus Golden-winged Parakeet					X
Graydidasculus brachyurus Short-tailed Parrot					X
Deroptyus accipitrinus Red-fan Parrot					X
Nyctibius bracteatus Rufous Potoo	X				
Chordeiles minor Common Nighthawk	X				X
Chaetura chapmani Chapman's Swift	X		X		X
Avocettula recurvirostris Fiery-tailed Awlbill					X
Popelairia popelairii Wire-crested Thorntail		X?			
Topaza pella Crimson Topaz					X
Trogon rufus Black-throated Trogon					X
Galbula cyanicollis Purple-necked Jacamar					X
Bucco capensis Collared Puffbird		X			X
Malacoptila rufa Rufous-necked Puffbird					X
Nonnula rubecula Rusty-breasted Nunlet					X
Monasa flavirostris Yellow-billed Nunbird	X		X	X	
Eubucco tucinkae Scarlet-hooded Barbet	X	X	X		
Deconychura stictolaema Spot-throated Woodcreeper					X
Dendrocolaptes hoffmannsi Hoffmann's Woodcreeper					X
Xiphorhynchus eytoni Dusky-billed Woodcreeper					X
Campylorhamphus procurvoides Curve-billed Scythebill					X
Synallaxis albigularis Dark-breasted Spinetail	X	X			
Certhiaxis mustelina Red-and-white Spinetail				X	
Automolus dorsalis Crested Foliage-gleaner	X	X	X		X
Xenops milleri Rufous-tailed Xenops	X	X			X
Frederickena unduligera Undulated Antshrike		X	X		
Sakesphorus luctuosus Glossy Antshrike					X
Thamnophilus murinus Mouse-colored Antshrike					X
Megastictus margaritatus Pearly Antshrike					X
Neoctantes niger Black Bushbird		X			
Clytoctantes sp. nov.					X
Thamnomanes caesius Cinereous Antshrike					X
Myrmotherula iheringi Ihering's Antwren	X	X			X
M. minor Salvadori's Antwren (probably *M. iheringi*?)				X	
Rhegmatorhina hoffmannsi White-breasted Antbird					X
Formicarius rufifrons Rufous-fronted Antthrush	X	X			
Myrmornis torquata Wing-banded Antpitta					X
Grallaria varia Variegated Antpitta					X
Grallaria eludens Elusive Antpitta		X?	X		

Species	Tpta	Manu	Balta	Purús	Rond
Conopophaga aurita Chestnut-belted Gnateater					X
Conopophaga peruviana Ash-throated Gnateater	X	X	X	X	
Liosceles thoracicus Rusty-belted Tapaculo		X	X		X
Mionectes olivaceus Olive-striped Flycatcher	X	X			
Poecilotriccus tricolor Tricolored Tody-Tyrant					X
Poecilotriccus albifacies White-cheeked Tody-Tyrant	X				
Platyrhynchus saturatus Cinnamon-crested Spadebill					X
Myiobius barbatus Sulphur-rumped Flycatcher		X	X	X	X
Xenopipo atronitens Black Manakin	X				
Porphyrolaema porphyrolaema Purple-throated Cotinga	X	X	X		
Xipholena punicea Pompadour Cotinga					X
Conioptilon mcilhennyi Black-faced Cotinga		X	X		
Haematoderus militaris Crimson Fruitcrow					X
Phoenicircus nigricollis Black-necked Red Cotinga					X
Atticora melanoleuca Black-collared Swallow					X
Odontorchilus cinereus Tooth-billed Wren					X
Microcerculus bambla Wing-banded Wren		X			
Catharus minimus Gray-cheeked Thrush	X				
Polioptila plumbea Tropical Gnatcatcher		X			
Polioptila guianensis Guianan Gnatcatcher					X
Vireo altiloquus Black-whiskered Vireo					X
Hylophilus muscicapinus Buff-cheeked Greenlet					X
Sporophila nigricollis Yellow-bellied Seedeater	X	X			
Sporophila americana Variable Seedeater		X			
Pheucticus ludovicianus Rose-breasted Grosbeak	X				
Conothraupis speculigera Black-and-white Tanager	X	X	X		
Tachyphonus surinamus Fulvous-crested Tanager					X
Cyanerpes nitidus Short-billed Honeycreeper					X
Conirostrum bicolor Bicolored Conebill					X
Dendroica striata Blackpoll Warbler	X				
Oporornis agilis Connecticut Warbler	X				
Wilsonia canadensis Canada Warbler	X				
Basileuterus chrysogaster Golden-bellied Warbler		X			
Cacicus koepckeae Selva Cacique		X?	X		
Psarocolius oseryi Casqued Oropendola	X	X			
Psarocolius viridis Green Oropendola					X
Agelaius xanthophthalmus Pale-eyed Blackbird	X	X			
Total number of species	25	23	15	5	46

* Tpta = Tambopata Reserve, Dpto. Madre de Dios, Peru (T. A. Parker, unpubl. data)
  Manu = Cocha Cashu Biological Station, Manu National Park, Dpto. Madre de Dios, Peru (Terborgh *et al.* 1984)
  Balta = Balta, Río Curanja, Dpto. Ucayali, Peru (O'Neill 1974)
  Purús = Alto Rio Purús (Bom Lugár, Monte Verde, Ponto Alegre), Dpto. Amazonas, Brazil (Gyldenstolpe 1951)
  Rond = Cachoeira Nazaré, Dpto. Rondonia, Brazil (D. F. Stotz *et al.*, unpubl. data)

regions in South America. Also, it must be kept in mind that such a scheme will be unsatisfactory for many species and for areas in the transition between "zones." Furthermore, human alteration of habitat has made it difficult to perceive the natural distributions of many species (T. A. Parker, pers. comm.). The scheme used here is an attempt to impose somewhat unrealistic typology on a continuous gradient and is therefore destined to be unsatisfactory in many cases. The use of "zones" herein is not meant as an endorsement of these zones as real units; they are used here mainly as a convenient "first approach" and to be consistent with much of the literature on distribution of Andean birds (e.g., Meyer de Schauensee 1966, 1970, 1982). A more sophisticated, quantitative scheme awaits more detailed data on habitat preferences and elevational ranges. (For detailed information on habitat preferences of those species that are also found in Peru, see Parker, Parker, and Plenge 1982). The life zones are as follows:

A = Amazonian lowland (below 1100 m) habitats of northern Bolivia, including "terra firme" forest up to 1100 m elevation, "varzea" forest and other riverine habitats (Remsen and Parker 1984), gallery forest within savanna regions, tongues of humid forest that occur along certain rivers and at the bases of small mountains in Dpto. Santa Cruz, and man-made second-growth. This corresponds roughly to the area shown as "lowland tropical forest" in Fig. 1. Detailed habitat preferences for Amazonian species are given by Remsen and Parker (1983) and Terborgh, Fitzpatrick, and Emmons (1984).

N = Non-Amazonian lowland habitats of central and southern Bolivia, from Dpto. Beni south, including savannas, grasslands, deciduous and partly deciduous forest, cerrado, and ranches. This corresponds roughly to the areas shown as "savanna," "semihumid lowland forest," and "chaco and deciduous forest" in Fig. 1.

L = Lowlands in general (A + N).

F = Foothills of the Andes in humid forest and second growth, 500-1100 m (dptos. La Paz, Cochabamba, and Santa Cruz only). This category is used only as a subset of "A" above and is listed only when a species has not yet been recorded away from the foothills.

U = Upper Tropical Zone of Meyer de Schauensee (1970): humid and semihumid forest and second growth 1100-1700 m on the humid eastern slope of the Andes.

S = Subtropical Zone of Meyer de Schauensee (1970): humid and semihumid forest and second growth 1700-2600 m on the humid eastern slope of the Andes.

T = Temperate Zone of Meyer de Schauensee (1970): humid and semihumid forest and second growth generally from 2600 to 3400-3600 m on the humid eastern slope of the Andes.

H = Humid Andean Forest: a combination of T, S, U, and occasionally F. This corresponds roughly to the areas shown as "humid montane forest" and "semihumid montane forest" in Fig. 1.

P = Puna Zone: open, treeless habitats above 3400-3700 m, consisting mainly of grassland, some brushlands, marshes, and lakes. This corresponds roughly to the areas shown as "altiplano" (the inter-Andean plateau), "salt flats," and "montane puna" in Fig. 1.

P/T = Area of transition between the treeless Puna Zone and forest of the Temperate Zone, usually 3400-3700 m, that consists of a mosaic of scrubby thickets, páramo-like vegetation, and scattered low trees interspersed with tall, wet grassy areas; it is found at timberline on the humid eastern slope and at high elevations in semihumid valleys. Also included here is *Polylepis* woodland (see Parker 1981 for characteristic bird species of *Polylepis* in Peru), although patches of *Polylepis* occur in higher and drier areas within the Puna Zone. Although many authors include this transition area in the Puna Zone, we separate it here because (1) many bird species are found only in this zone, or in this zone and "T" or "V", and (2) the number of non-"W" species (see below) shared with the higher and drier Puna is small (12 of 70, 17%).

V = "Valle" zone: the semi-arid and arid intermontane valleys of the Andes from 1000-3600 m, where the habitat is dominated by shrubs and grassland with trees restricted to immediate vicinity of watercourses. (Further field work may show that this zone should be divided into two, an upper and lower, with the break at about 2500 m, many lowland species seem to range up to about 2500 m and many high elevation species do not occur below this elevation). This corresponds roughly to the area shown as "semiarid intermontane valleys" in Fig. 1.

W = Widespread, occurring in more than 3-4 zones (excluding "H" species).

The number of species in each major zone, and the number of species found only within that zone (including migrants), is given in Table 2. Although the Amazonian lowlands are the least known area of Bolivia, they are by far the richest zone: almost 50% of the bird species of Bolivia are found there. The Humid Andean Forest has the highest

Table 2. Number of bird species in the "life zones" (*) of Bolivia. The first column gives the total number of species found in the zone, the second column presents the number of species restricted to that zone, the third column gives the percent of the species in that zone that are restricted to it, and the fourth column gives the percent of the total number of species known from Bolivia found in that zone. All totals include widespread ("W") species found in that zone.

Life zone (codes*)	# species	# restricted spp.	% restricted	% total
Lowlands of Amazonia (A + L)	601	392	65%	47%
Lowlands outside Amazonia (N + L)	403	168	42%	32%
Humid Andean Forest (U + S + T + H)	285	201	71%	22%
Upper Tropical Zone (U + H)	194	72	37%	15%
Valle Zone (V)	180	42	23%	14%
Subtropical Zone (S + H)	128	26	20%	10%
Puna Zone (P)	126	72	57%	10%
Temperate Zone (T + H)	96	25	26%	8%
Transition Puna-to-Temperate (P/T)	75	20	27%	6%

* See text pp. 14-15 for descriptions of life zones and codes.

per cent of species restricted to it. Of the zones with relatively limited areal extent, the Upper Tropical Zone is the richest. Table 3 presents the number of species (including migrants) that show particular distribution patterns with respect to the life zone designations given for each species in the far right column of the main bird list. (Only patterns with more than 20 species are presented in Table 3). Some salient points from Table 3 are: (1) more than twice as many species show the "Amazonian-lowlands" pattern than the next most frequent pattern, and nearly one-third of all Bolivian birds show the "Amazon only" pattern; (2) the similarity in species composition of the Upper Tropical and Subtropical and the Subtropical and Temperate zones is evident from the high number of species found in various combinations of the three; and (3) the similarity of the Valle Zone avifauna to that of the lowlands is indicated by the high number of species with "L,V" or "N,V" patterns.

The main checklist is followed by a "hypothetical list" that includes species that: (1) have been published as occurring in Bolivia, but the record is erroneous; (2) have been published as occurring in Bolivia, but for which we can find no specimen or published locality record; although many of these will probably be found to occur in Bolivia, we prefer a cautious approach until positive evidence is obtained; and (3) sight or sound records that require further confirmation.

Table 3. Most frequent "life zone" distribution patterns for bird species in Bolivia, with percent of total number of species known from Bolivia for each pattern.

Zone pattern (codes*)	Number of species	% total
Amazonian lowlands (A)	404	32%
Non-Amazonian lowlands (N)	169	13%
Lowlands (L)	115	9%
Puna (P)	72	6%
Upper Tropical Zone (U)	72	6%
Valle Zone (V)	42	3%
Lowlands + Valle (L,V or V,L)	36	3%
Subtropical + Temperate zones (S,T or T,S)	33	3%
Upper Tropical + Subtropical zones (U,S or S,U)	32	3%
Non-Amazonian Lowlands + Valle (N,V or V,N)	32	3%
Subtropical Zone (S)	26	2%
Temperate Zone (T)	25	2%
Andean Foothills (F)	22	2%

* See text pp. 14-15 for codes and descriptions of life zones.

Acknowledgments

Remsen is grateful to the late Babette Odom, John S. McIlhenny, and Dr. H. Irving and Laura Schweppe for their support of the recent LSU fieldwork in Bolivia. We thank the Dirección de Ciencia y Tecnología, La Paz, through Ing. Carlos Aguirre and Dr. Arturo Castaños, the Academia Nacional de Ciencias, through Dr. Ovidio Suárez Morales and Ing. Antonio Saavedra Muños, and the Parque Nacional Noel Kempff Mercado, through Ing. Néstor Ruiz I. and Abel Castillo, for facilitating our work in Bolivia. Prof. Gastón Bejarano deserves special thanks for his aid to field work in Bolivia. Eliana Flores, Bruce and Helen Glick, the Groves Construction Company, Tom and Jo Heindel, Carlos E. and M. Dolores Quintela, Dr. Enrique Quintela, and Dr. James Solomon have all provided invaluable assistance to LSU fieldwork in Bolivia. We thank Dr. Kenneth C. Parkes (Carnegie Museum of Natural History), Dr. Ralph B. Schreiber (Los Angeles County Museum of Natural History), Mark B. Robbins and Frank B. Gill (Academy of Natural Sciences of Philadelphia), and Richard C. Banks (U.S. National Museum) for information on Bolivian specimens in their care. J. Cabot, S. E. Davis, J. Fjeldså, N. Krabbe, T. Maxwell, L. Short, and F. Vuilleumier generously provided us with information from their unpublished manuscripts and notes. Alice J. Fogg accurately and painstakingly typed the original manuscript with initial help from Mark S. Hafner; Jana Kloss converted the original draft's computer diskettes to IBM format for publication. Carlos E. Quintela prepared Fig. 1. We thank Steven W. Cardiff, Robin O. S. Clarke, John A. Gerwin, Bruce D. Glick, Burt L. Monroe, Jr., John P. O'Neill, Carlos E. Quintela, T. A. Parker III, Kenneth C. Parkes, Robert S. Ridgely, Kenneth V. Rosenberg, C. Gregory Schmitt, Donna C. Schmitt, Thomas S. Schulenberg, and D. F. Stotz for their comments on the manuscript or portions thereof.

MAIN LIST

LIST OF SYMBOLS FOR QUICK REFERENCE

Bird Name columns

      numbers in parenthesis after a scientific name refer to the footnotes
      in the Taxonomic Footnotes section [see pp. 52-55].
      (N)--after an English name indicates that the species is a migrant
      from North America.

Departamento columns

      Numbers refer to numbered citations
        in the Literature Citations [pp. 62-73]
      Numbers in parentheses refer to citations that
        do not provide a precise locality for that species
        within that departamento.
      *--indicates a sight record [see p. 11].
      ‡--indicates that the record is supported by a
        photograph or sound recording.

Life Zones column [for details see pp. 14-15]

    A = Amazonian lowlands
    N = Non-Amazonian lowlands
    L = Lowlands in general
    F = Andean foothills
    U = Upper Tropical Zone
    S = Subtropical Zone
    T = Temperate Zone
    H = T + S + U + occasionally F
    P = Puna Zone
    P/T = Puna/Temperate transition
    V = Valle zone
    W = widespread

	Pando	Beni	La Paz	Cochabamba	Santa Cruz	Chuquisaca	Tarija	Oruro	Potosí	life zone
RHEIDAE (rheas; 2 species)										
Rhea americana. Greater Rhea		33			50		52			N
Pterocnemia pennata. Lesser Rhea			79					79	9	P
TINAMIDAE (tinamous; 21 species)										
Tinamus tao. Gray Tinamou	33		16	9	120					A
Tinamus major. Great Tinamou	89*	33	9	9	120					A
Tinamus guttatus. White-throated Tinamou	33	33								A
Nothocercus nigrocapillus. Hooded Tinamou			9	120						H
Crypturellus cinereus. Cinereous Tinamou	33	9	9							A
Crypturellus soui. Little Tinamou	33	9	9		120					A
Crypturellus obsoletus. Brown Tinamou	89‡		9	9	9					U,S,A
Crypturellus undulatus. Undulated Tinamou	33	9	58	9	62					L
Crypturellus strigulosus. Brazilian Tinamou	33				2a					A
Crypturellus atrocapillus. Black-capped Tinamou			9	9	120					U
Crypturellus variegatus. Variegated Tinamou	66									A
Crypturellus bartletti. Bartlett's Tinamou	33	33	65a*							A
Crypturellus parvirostris. Small-billed Tinamou		33	16		120					N
Crypturellus tataupa. Tataupa Tinamou		33	9		9	9	9			N
Rhynchotus rufescens. Red-winged Tinamou		9	9	120	9	9	93			N,V
Nothoprocta ornata. Ornate Tinamou			120	9		13a		9	9	P
Nothoprocta cinerascens. Brushland Tinamou						13a	9			N
Nothoprocta pentlandii. Andean Tinamou			9	9	120	9	93		9	V,P/T
Nothura boraquira. White-bellied Nothura					9					N
Nothura darwinii. Darwin's Nothura			120	9	13a	13a*	9	9		P
Tinamotis pentlandii. Puna Tinamou								100	9	P
PODICIPEDIDAE (grebes; 5 species)										
Rollandia rolland. White-tufted Grebe			9	58	101		52	9		P,N
Rollandia microptera. Short-winged Grebe			58					9		P
Tachybaptus dominicus. Least Grebe			59	93	93	93	98			N
Podilymbus podiceps. Pied-billed Grebe				90	90	92	92			N
Podiceps occipitalis. Silvery Grebe				45				53	9	P
PHALACROCORACIDAE (cormorants; 1 species)										
Phalacrocorax brasilianis.(1) Olivaceous Cormorant		33*	58*	45	45		9	58*		W
ANHINGIDAE (anhingas; 1 species)										
Anhinga anhinga. Anhinga		1	58	85*	93					L
ARDEIDAE (herons; 15 species)										
Ixobrychus involucris. Stripe-backed Bittern					19a		98			N
Ixobrychus exilis. Least Bittern		9								A
Zebrilus undulatus. Zigzag Heron		75			2a					A
Tigrisoma fasciatum. Fasciated Tiger-Heron			16	62	93					F,U
Tigrisoma lineatum. Rufescent Tiger-Heron	33	33	65a*	45	45		98			L
Syrigma sibilatrix. Whistling Heron		33			9		50			N
Pilherodius pileatus. Capped Heron	33	1	9	93	50					A
Ardea cocoi. Cocoi Heron	89*	33	58*	58*	45		52			L

	Pando	Beni	La Paz	Cochabamba	Santa Cruz	Chuquisaca	Tarija	Oruro	Potosí	life zone
Casmerodius albus. Great Egret		33	85*	58	9	93	26			L
Bubulcus ibis. Cattle Egret		76*	59	85*	101	100*	60*			L
Egretta thula. Snowy Egret		33	58	58	45					L
Butorides striatus. Striated Heron	89*	33	93	93	9	93	98			L
Agamia agami. Chestnut-bellied Heron	33			93	45					A
Nycticorax nycticorax. Black-crowned Night-Heron		33	58	9	9		98	9		N,P
Cochlearius cochlearius. Boat-billed Heron		33*	13a	93	56					A
PHOENICOPTERIDAE (flamingos; 3 species)										
Phoenicopterus chilensis. Chilean Flamingo			45	93	16a*		9	9	77	P
Phoenicoparrus andinus. Andean Flamingo								100*	77	P
Phoenicoparrus jamesi. James' Flamingo			58					9	77	P
THRESKIORNITHIDAE (ibises; 8 species)										
Phimosus infuscatus. Bare-faced Ibis		33			9					N
Plegadis chihi. White-faced Ibis				45		163	52			N
Plegadis ridgwayi. Puna Ibis			45	45		16		9		P
Theristicus caerulescens. Plumbeous Ibis		33					52			N
Theristicus caudatus. Buff-necked Ibis		9		45	50	9	26			N
Theristicus melanopis. Black-faced Ibis			33	16						P
Mesembrinibis cayennensis. Green Ibis	33	33	65a*	85*	45					L
Platalea ajaja. Roseate Spoonbill		33	87		45		9*			N
CICONIIDAE (storks; 3 species)										
Mycteria americana. Wood Stork	89*	33	58		45		26			L
Ciconia maguari. Maguari Stork		33		93	19a*		52			N
Jabiru mycteria. Jabiru	33	33	65a*		93		26			L
CATHARTIDAE (vultures; 6 species)										
Coragyps atratus. Black Vulture	89*	76*	58*	47	47		9*			L
Cathartes aura. Turkey Vulture	89*	33	58	9	47	13a*	9			W
Cathartes burrovianus. Lesser Yellow-headed Vulture		100		90*	101*					N
Cathartes melambrotus. Greater Yellow-headed Vulture	89	76*	65a*		56					A
Vultur gryphus. Andean Condor			83*	9	93	9	60*		53	P,V,P/
Sarcoramphus papa. King Vulture	89*	33	9*	58*	50		9*			L
ANHIMIDAE (screamers; 2 species)										
Anhima cornuta. Horned Screamer	89‡	33	65a*		9					A
Chauna torquta. Southern Screamer		33		85*	9	93	52			N
ANATIDAE (waterfowl; 21 species)										
Dendrocygna bicolor. Fulvous Whistling-Duck		100*		13a*	90		92			N
Dendrocygna viduata. White-faced Whistling-Duck		33			9					N
Dendrocygna autumnalis. Black-bellied Whistling-Duck		33		23*	9	93	93			N
Chloephaga melanoptera. Andean Goose			9	45				100*	13a	P
Neochen jubata. Orinoco Goose		33	58	9	45		52			L
Cairina moschata. Muscovy Duck	89*	33	58	93	9	93	52			L

	Pando	Beni	La Paz	Cochabamba	Santa Cruz	Chuquisaca	Tarija	Oruro	Potosí	life zone
Callonetta leucophrys. Ringed Teal		100*			9	93	52			N
Amazonetta brasiliensis. Brazilian Duck		33			9		52			N
Merganetta armata. Torrent Duck			58	9		93	45		53	T,S,P/T
Anas flavirostris. Speckled Teal			53	45				53	9	P,V
Anas specularioides. Crested Duck			58	45			45	9	9	P
Anas georgica. Yellow-billed Pintail			58	45			45	53	9	P
Anas bahamensis. White-cheeked Pintail				23*	45	93	93	9		P,V,L
Anas versicolor. Silver Teal			58	45			52	9	77	P
Anas cyanoptera. Cinnamon Teal			1	93				100*	13a	P,V
Anas platalea. Red Shoveler			(56)		(56)		52			N
Netta peposaca. Rosy-billed Pochard					93					N
Heteronetta atricapilla. Black-headed Duck					56					N
Oxyura dominica. Masked Duck					101	93	52			N
Oxyura jamaicensis. Ruddy Duck			58	9	101			9		P,V
Sarkidiornis melanotos. Comb Duck				23*	93					N,V
ACCIPITRIDAE (hawks; 45 species)										
Pandion haliaetus. Osprey (N)		76*	13*	90*	93					A
Leptodon cayanensis. Gray-headed Kite	89‡	9	65a*	93	47					A
Chondrohierax uncinatus. Hook-billed Kite	89*	33	87*		31					A
Elanoides forficatus. Swallow-tailed Kite	89*	33	58	93	35		9*			L,U
Gampsonyx swainsonii. Pearl Kite					47		52			N
Elanus caeruleus. Black-shouldered Kite		100*			90*	90*	90*			N,V
Rostrhamus sociabilis. Snail Kite		33		85*	93	93	93			N
Rostrhamus hamatus. Slender-billed Kite		13								A
Harpagus bidentatus. Double-toothed Kite	89*	13	65a*		35					A
Harpagus diodon. Rufous-thighed Kite					63					A
Ictinia mississippiensis. Mississippi Kite (N)					106					N
Ictinia plumbea. Plumbeous Kite	33	33	9	9	50		9			L
Circus cinereus. Cinereous Harrier			58	9	68*			9		P
Circus buffoni. Long-winged Harrier		33			35					N
Accipiter poliogaster. Gray-bellied Hawk	33				47					A
Accipiter superciliosus. Tiny Hawk				85*	90					A
Accipiter striatus. Sharp-shinned Hawk			59	9	35	93	9			T,S,N
Accipiter bicolor. Bicolored Hawk	89*		58		35	93	9			L
Geranospiza caerulescens. Crane Hawk	89*	76*	65a*		35	93	9			L
Leucopternis schistacea. Slate-colored Hawk	33	58	65a*	9	47					A
Leucopternis kuhli. White-browed Hawk	66*									A
Leucopternis albicollis. White Hawk			86*		47					F
Asturina nitida. Gray Hawk	89	33			50					A
Buteogallus urubitinga. Great Black Hawk	89*	33	87*	93	35	93	9			L
Buteogallus meridionalis. Savanna Hawk		9			50	93	9			N
Parabuteo unicinctus. Harris' Hawk		33	16	16?	35	93	50			N
Busarellus nigricollis. Black-collared Hawk	33	9		85*	35					A
Geranoaetus melanoleucus. Black-chested Buzzard-Eagle			93*	9	68*	9				V,P

	Pando	Beni	La Paz	Cochabamba	Santa Cruz	Chuquisaca	Tarija	Oruro	Potosí	life zone
Harpyhaliaetus solitarius. Solitary Eagle			86*	90	90*					U
Harpyhaliaetus coronatus. Crowned Eagle	"Bolivia" (47)									N
Buteo magnirostris. Roadside Hawk	33	9	9	9	9	9	9			L,V
Buteo leucorrhous. White-rumped Hawk			67*	67						S,T
Buteo platypterus. Broad-winged Hawk (N)			13a	(56)	93					L
Buteo brachyurus. Short-tailed Hawk	89*		59	13	47					A
Buteo swainsoni. Swainson's Hawk (N)		76*			56		93			L
Buteo albicaudatus. White-tailed Hawk		84*			47	9	93			N
Buteo polyosoma. Red-backed Hawk			59	16	13a	13a*	52	16		V,P
Buteo poecilochrous. Puna Hawk			133	9				9	13a	P
Buteo albonotatus. Zone-tailed Hawk	89*				47					L
Morphnus guianensis. Crested Eagle					47					A
Harpia harpyja. Harpy Eagle				35	35					A
Spizastur melanoleucus. Black-and-white Hawk-Eagle			90*	68*	90*	90				A
Spizaetus tyrannus. Black Hawk-Eagle	89*	(56)	86*		47					A
Spizaetus ornatus. Ornate Hawk-Eagle	33	33	65a*	29						A
Oroaetus isidori. Black-and-chestnut Eagle			16	68*						U,S

FALCONIDAE (falcons; 16 species)

	Pando	Beni	La Paz	Cochabamba	Santa Cruz	Chuquisaca	Tarija	Oruro	Potosí	life zone
Daptrius ater. Black Caracara		33	87*	93	93					A
Daptrius americanus. Red-throated Caracara	89‡	100*	9		93					A
Phalcoboenus megalopterus. Mountain Caracara			9	35		13a*	60*	13a*	9	P,P/T
Polyborus plancus. Crested Caracara		33			93	93	26			N
Milvago chimachima. Yellow-headed Caracara		33		9	9	93				L
Herpetotheres cachinnans. Laughing Falcon	89*	33		85*	9	93	98			L
Micrastur ruficollis. Barred Forest-Falcon	89		86	62	19a					U,S,A
Micrastur gilvicollis.(2) Lined Forest-Falcon	89		87	35	9					A
Micrastur mirandollei. Slaty-backed Forest-Falcon			9							F
Micrastur semitorquatus. Collared Forest-Falcon		33		93	47		52			L
Spiziapteryx circumcinctus. Spot-winged Falconet					12					N
Falco sparverius. American Kestrel		33	9	9	9	9	9	9	9	W
Falco femoralis. Aplomado Falcon		33	9	47	9	35	9	16	9	P,N
Falco rufigularis. Bat Falcon	89*	85	9	9	50	93	9			L
Falco peregrinus. Peregrine Falcon			11	11	90*		52	90*		W
Falco deiroleucus. Orange-breasted Falcon			13	90						L

CRACIDAE (3) (guans; 14 species)

	Pando	Beni	La Paz	Cochabamba	Santa Cruz	Chuquisaca	Tarija	Oruro	Potosí	life zone
Ortalis canicollis. Chaco Chachalaca					101	93	9			N
Ortalis motmot. Speckled Chachalaca	33	9	9	9	9					L
Penelope montagnii. Andean Guan			9	9	9					H
Penelope superciliaris. Rusty-margined Guan					92					L
Penelope dabbenei. Red-faced Guan						9	93			S
Penelope obscura. Dusky-legged Guan				44	9	9	9			V
Penelope jacquacu. Spix's Guan	33	9	86	33	9					A
Pipile pipile. Blue-throated Piping-Guan		9	9	9	9					A
Pipile cujubi. Red-throated Piping-Guan					2a					A

	Pando	Beni	La Paz	Cochabamba	Santa Cruz	Chuquisaca	Tarija	Oruro	Potosi	life zone
Chamaepetes goudotii. Sickle-winged Guan			14							T
Mitu tuberosa. Greater Razor-billed Curassow		33	9	9	44					A
Pauxi unicornis. Horned Curassow				9	18a*					U
Crax globulosa. Wattled Curassow		33								A
Crax fasciolata. Bare-faced Curassow		93			50					N

PHASIANIDAE (quail; 4 species)

	Pando	Beni	La Paz	Cochabamba	Santa Cruz	Chuquisaca	Tarija	Oruro	Potosi	life zone
Odontophorus gujanensis. Marbled Wood-Quail			9	9	44					F
Odontophorus speciosus.										
Rufous-breasted Wood-Quail			86	93	9					U
Odontophorus ballivjani. Stripe-faced Wood-Quail			83*	9						T
Odontophorus stellatus. Starred Wood-Quail	33		65a*		2a‡					A

RALLIDAE (rails; 20 species)

	Pando	Beni	La Paz	Cochabamba	Santa Cruz	Chuquisaca	Tarija	Oruro	Potosi	life zone
Rallus sanguinolentus. Plumbeous Rail			9	93	101		9			V,P
Rallus nigricans. Blackish Rail	66*									A
Pardirallus maculatus. Spotted Rail					73					N
Amaurolimnas concolor. Uniform Crake					44					A
Aramides cajanea. Gray-necked Wood-Rail	89	9	16	9	9		9			L
Anurolimnas castaneiceps. Chestnut-headed Crake	66									A
Porzana albicollis. Ash-throated Crake		9			44					N
Porzana flaviventer. Yellow-breasted Crake					68*					N
Laterallus exilis. Gray-breasted Crake			103							A
Laterallus melanophaius. Rufous-sided Crake	89	76*			104					A
Micropygia schomburgkii. Ocellated Crake		53?								N
Neocrex erythrops. Paint-billed Crake			92		92					N,V
Porphyriops melanops. Spot-flanked Gallinule					104		52			N
Gallinula chloropus. Common Moorhen			58	129	93	93	52		9	N,P
Porphyrula martinica. Purple Gallinule		85*	58		44					A
Porphyrula flavirostris. Azure Gallinule		33			93					A
Fulica ardesiaca.(4) Slate-colored Coot			58	44				9	9	P,V
Fulica leucoptera. White-winged Coot					104	93	52			N
Fulica gigantea. Giant Coot			44	9			52*	100*	9	P
Fulica cornuta. Horned Coot								53	104	P

HELIORNITHIDAE (sungrebes; 1 species)

	Pando	Beni	La Paz	Cochabamba	Santa Cruz	Chuquisaca	Tarija	Oruro	Potosi	life zone
Heliornis fulica. Sungrebe		33	13a*	93	93		93			L

EURYPYGIDAE (sunbittern; 1 species)

	Pando	Beni	La Paz	Cochabamba	Santa Cruz	Chuquisaca	Tarija	Oruro	Potosi	life zone
Eurypyga helias. Sunbittern	89*	9	16	9	9					A

CARIAMIDAE (seriemas; 2 species)

	Pando	Beni	La Paz	Cochabamba	Santa Cruz	Chuquisaca	Tarija	Oruro	Potosi	life zone
Cariama cristata. Red-legged Seriema					56	100*	100*			N
Chunga burmeisteri. Black-legged Seriema					101	99	26			N

ARAMIDAE (limpkin; 1 species)

	Pando	Beni	La Paz	Cochabamba	Santa Cruz	Chuquisaca	Tarija	Oruro	Potosi	life zone
Aramus guarauna. Limpkin			9	58	93	44	93	52		N

PSOPHIIDAE (trumpeters; 1 species)

	Pando	Beni	La Paz	Cochabamba	Santa Cruz	Chuquisaca	Tarija	Oruro	Potosi	life zone
Psophia leucoptera. Pale-winged Trumpeter	89	33	16		9					A

CHARADRIIDAE (plovers, 10 species)

	Pando	Beni	La Paz	Cochabamba	Santa Cruz	Chuquisaca	Tarija	Oruro	Potosi	life zone
Vanellus cyaneus. Pied Lapwing	33	33	58	85*	9					A

	Pando	Beni	La Paz	Cochabamba	Santa Cruz	Chuquisaca	Tarija	Oruro	Potosí	life zone
Vanellus chilensis. Southern Lapwing		33			46	93	9			N
Vanellus resplendens. Andean Lapwing			9	46		13a*		53	9	P
Pluvialis dominica. Lesser Golden-Plover (N)		76*	93	46	9	93	9	93*		L,P
Pluvialis squatarola. Black-bellied Plover (N)					101*					N
Charadrius semipalmatus. Semipalmated Plover (N)							52			N
Charadrius collaris. Collared Plover	33	33	93	9	46		9			L,V
Charadrius falklandicus. Two-banded Plover			58	46			46	9	9	P
Phegornis mitchellii. Diademed Sandpiper-Plover			9						9	P
Eudromias ruficollis. Tawny-throated Dotterel			58	46				16	9	P
RECURVIROSTRIDAE (avocets; 2 species)										
Himantopus mexicanus. Black-necked Stilt			13a*85*	46			52	9		N,V
Recurvirostra andina. Andean Avocet			46	46				9	9	P
JACANIDAE (jacanas; 1 species)										
Jacana jacana. Wattled Jacana	33	9	58	13a*50		93	9			L
SCOLOPACIDAE (sandpipers; 17 species)										
Limosa haemastica. Hudsonian Godwit (N)				13a*68*				75‡		P,N
Bartramia longicauda. Upland Sandpiper (N)	33	9	59	93	93		52	68*		L,P
Numenius phaeopus. Whimbrel (N)								27*		P
Tringa melanoleuca. Greater Yellowlegs (N)		1	94	46	93			100		L,P
Tringa flavipes. Lesser Yellowlegs (N)		33	58	46	50		9	9	9	L,P
Tringa solitaria. Solitary Sandpiper (N)	33	76*	65a*	9	50	93	98			L
Actitis macularia. Spotted Sandpiper (N)		1	13a	46	46		98			L
Phalaropus tricolor. Wilson's Phalarope (N)		58	58	46	101*	93	93	93		P,L
Gallinago paraguaiae. South American Snipe		33	58	9	46		46	9	9	N,P
Gallinago jamesoni. Andean Snipe			83	134						P/T
Calidris canutus. Red Knot (N)			21*							P
Calidris minutilla. Least Sandpiper (N)		33			101*					L
Calidris fuscicollis. White-rumped Sandpiper (N)	33	33			50					L
Calidris bairdii. Baird's Sandpiper (N)			58	46	50			9	9	P,V
Calidris melanotos. Pectoral Sandpiper (N)	33	33	9	46	50	93	26	75*	9	L,P,V
Calidris himantopus. Stilt Sandpiper (N)		1	93	46	93			9		P,L
Tryngites subruficollis. Buff-breasted Sandpiper (N)	33	33			68*					L
THINOCORIDAE (seedsnipe; 3 species)										
Attagis gayi. Rufous-bellied Seedsnipe			9	9					13a	P
Thinocorus orbignyianus. Gray-breasted Seedsnipe			9	93				9	9	P
Thinocorus rumicivorus. Least Seedsnipe			46					46	9	P
LARIDAE (gulls; 5 species)										
Larus serranus. Andean Gull			9	9				9	77	P,V
Larus pipixcan. Franklin's Gull (N)			90*						13a	P
Phaetusa simplex. Large-billed Tern	89*	33	58	9	93					A
Sterna hirundo. Common Tern (N)		90*		90	101*					L
Sterna superciliaris. Yellow-billed Tern	89*	33	58	68*	93					A
RYNCHOPIDAE (skimmers; 1 species)										
Rynchops niger. Black Skimmer			9?	58	13a*93			68*		A

	Pando	Beni	La Paz	Cochabamba	Santa Cruz	Chuquisaca	Tarija	Oruro	Potosí	life zone
COLUMBIDAE (pigeons; 23 species)										
Columba speciosa. Scaled Pigeon	33	58	9		44					A
Columba picazuro. Picazuro Pigeon		33			9		9			N
Columba maculosa. Spot-winged Pigeon			94*	9	44	16	52		9	P/T,V
Columba fasciata. Band-tailed Pigeon			9	9	68*					T,S
Columba cayennensis. Pale-vented Pigeon	33	9	9	33	9		9			L
Columba plumbea. Plumbeous Pigeon	33	33	9	9	119					U,A
Columba subvinacea. Ruddy Pigeon	89‡	33	9	9	9					A
Zenaida auriculata. Eared Dove		1	9	9	9	16	9		9	W
Columbina minuta. Plain-breasted Ground-Dove		33	87		94					N
Columbina talpacoti. Ruddy Ground-Dove	33	9	58	94	109		9			L
Columbina picui. Picui Ground-Dove	89	9	9	9	9	16	9		9	W
Claravis pretiosa. Blue Ground-Dove	33	33	9	9	9		9			L
Claravis mondetoura.										
Maroon-chested Ground-Dove			44	9						H
Metriopelia ceciliae. Bare-faced Ground-Dove			9	9		16	94	9	9	V,P
Metriopelia melanoptera.										
Black-winged Ground-Dove			58	9		16		9	9	P/T,V
Metriopelia aymara. Golden-spotted Ground-Dove			94	16		60*		9	9	P
Uropelia campestris. Long-tailed Ground-Dove		33			44					N
Leptotila verreauxi. White-tipped Dove	89*	33	9	9	50	9	9			L,V
Leptotila megalura. Large-tailed Dove			9	9	9	9	9			S,U
Leptotila rufaxilla. Gray-fronted Dove	33	33	9	9	44					A
Geotrygon frenata. White-throated Quail-Dove			9	9	9		9			S
Geotrygon violacea. Violaceous Quail-Dove	89	100	9		44					F
Geotrygon montana. Ruddy Quail-Dove	33	33	9	9	44					A
PSITTACIDAE (parrots; 46 species)										
Anodorhynchus hyacinthinus. Hyacinthine Macaw					90					N
Ara ararauna. Blue-and-yellow Macaw	89*	9	65a*	94	48					L
Ara glaucogularis.(5) Blue-throated Macaw		48?			48		48?			N
Ara militaris. Military Macaw					94	9	94			F
Ara macao. Scarlet Macaw	89*	23*	65a*	23*	104					A
Ara chloroptera. Red-and-green Macaw		9	87*	94	50					A
Ara rubrogenys. Red-fronted Macaw				9	94					V
Ara auricollis. Golden-collared Macaw		33			9	100*	9			N
Ara severa. Chestnut-fronted Macaw	33	33	9	9	9					A
Ara manilata. Red-bellied Macaw	89*	75*	65a*		90					L
Ara couloni. Blue-headed Macaw	66‡									A
Ara nobilis. Red-shouldered Macaw		90*	65a*		19a					N
Aratinga acuticauda. Blue-crowned Parakeet				9	9	9	52			N
Aratinga mitrata. Mitred Parakeet			104	94	9	13a*	9			V
Aratinga leucophthalmus. White-eyed Parakeet	89	9	87*	9	9	94	52			L
Aratinga weddellii. Dusky-headed Parakeet	33	33	65a*	9	104					A
Aratinga aurea. Peach-fronted Parakeet		9	65a*		19					N
Pyrrhura molinae. Green-cheeked Parakeet		9	9	9	9	9	9			N,U

	Pando	Beni	La Paz	Cochabamba	Santa Cruz	Chuquisaca	Tarija	Oruro	Potosí	life zone
Pyrrhura rhodogaster. Crimson-bellied Parakeet					2a					A
Pyrrhura picta. Painted Parakeet			9		2a					A
Pyrrhura rupicola. Rock Parakeet	89	33	1							A
Myiopsitta monachus. Monk Parakeet				9	94	94	50			N,V
Bolborhynchus aymara. Gray-hooded Parakeet			104	9	94	9	9		9	V
Bolborhynchus aurifrons. Mountain Parakeet			94	9				9	9	P
Bolborhynchus orbygnesius. Andean Parakeet			97	9						P/T
Forpus xanthopterygius. Blue-winged Parrotlet		33		68*	9					L
Forpus sclateri. Dusky-billed Parrotlet	33		65a*		94					A
Brotogeris versicolurus. Canary-winged Parakeet		9		9	9		57			L,V
Brotogeris cyanoptera. Cobalt-winged Parakeet	33	9	94	9	94					A
Brotogeris sanctithomae. Tui Parakeet	33	33								A
Nannopsittaca sp. nov.(6)			65a*							A
Touit huetii. Scarlet-shouldered Parrotlet	66‡		65a*							A
Pionites leucogaster. White-bellied Parrot	89	33	87*		94					A
Pionopsitta barrabandi. Orange-cheeked Parrot	89	90*	65a*							A
Hapalopsittaca melanotis. Black-eared Parrot			104	9						T
Pionus menstruus. Blue-headed Parrot	33	33	9	9	94					A
Pionus sordidus. Red-billed Parrot			58	9	9					U,S
Pionus maximiliani. Scaly-headed Parrot		33			9	9	9			N
Pionus tumultuosus. Plum-crowned Parrot			104	9	13a*					T,S
Amazona tucumana. Alder Parrot						9	9			S,U
Amazona xanthops. Yellow-faced Parrot					94					N
Amazona aestiva. Turquoise-fronted Parrot		33		9	9	94	9			L,V
Amazona ochrocephala. Yellow-headed Parrot	89	90	65a*		2a*					A
Amazona amazonica. Orange-winged Parrot		94		9	9					L
Amazona mercenaria. Scaly-naped Parrot			9	9	94					H
Amazona farinosa. Mealy Parrot	89	76*	9	9	9					A
CUCULIDAE (cuckoos; 15 species)										
Coccyzus cinereus. Ash-colored Cuckoo		33			9		98			L
Coccyzus erythropthalmus. Black-billed Cuckoo (N)				90	92					L,V
Coccyzus americanus. Yellow-billed Cuckoo (N)		33	59	94	94		50			L,V
Coccyzus euleri.(7) Pearly-breasted Cuckoo					94					N
Coccyzus melacoryphus. Dark-billed Cuckoo	89	33	33	33	9		9			L
Piaya cayana. Squirrel Cuckoo	33	33	33	9	9	9	9			L,U
Piaya melanogaster. Black-bellied Cuckoo	66									A
Piaya minuta. Little Cuckoo	33	33	87	9	16a*					A
Crotophaga major. Greater Ani	33	33		85*	94					A
Crotophaga ani. Smooth-billed Ani	33	33	58	9	50	94	52			L
Guira guira. Guira Cuckoo		9		9	9	94	9			N,V
Tapera naevia. Striped Cuckoo	33	9	87	94	9		26			L
Dromococcyx phasianellus. Pheasant Cuckoo	89‡	76	87*	9	2a*					A
Dromococcyx pavoninus. Pavonine Cuckoo	89‡		92		90					U,A
Neomorphus geoffroyi. Rufous-vented Ground-Cuckoo	89		9		2a*					A,U

	Pando	Beni	La Paz	Cochabamba	Santa Cruz	Chuquisaca	Tarija	Oruro	Potosí	life zone
OPISTHOCOMIDAE (hoatzin; 1 species)										
Opisthocomus hoazin. Hoatzin	89	33		9	94					A
TYTONIDAE (barn owls; 1 species)										
Tyto alba. Barn Owl		33	58	9	58		26			N,V
STRIGIDAE (owls; 19 species)										
Otus guatemalae. Vermiculated Screech-Owl				9						F
Otus choliba. Tropical Screech-Owl	89	33	28	9	9	9	50			L
Otus ingens.(8) Rufescent Screech-Owl			9	94						U
Otus watsonii. Tawny-bellied Screech-Owl	33	76*	87		101					A
Otus albogularis. White-throated Screech-Owl				9						T
Lophostrix cristata. Crested Owl	89‡	33	65a*		2a*					A
Bubo virginianus. Great Horned Owl		33	9	9	35			9		P,V,N?
Pulsatrix perspicillata. Spectacled Owl	89‡	76*	65a*	94	35		52			L
Pulsatrix melanota. Band-bellied Owl			86‡	126						U
Glaucidium minutissimum Least Pygmy-Owl	66		65a*							A
Glaucidium jardinii. Andean Pygmy-Owl			59	9						H
Glaucidium brasilianum. Ferruginous Pygmy-Owl	33	9	87	9	9	94	9			L
Speotyto cunicularia. Burrowing Owl			58		35		52	13a	9	N,P
Ciccaba virgata. Mottled Owl			9	(56)	94					A
Ciccaba huhula. Black-banded Owl			92		74					L,U
Ciccaba albitarsus. Rufous-banded Owl				126						S,T
Rhinoptynx clamator. Striped Owl		9	59		94					L
Asio flammeus. Short-eared Owl				94						V
Aegolius harrisi. Buff-fronted Owl					92					S,N
STEATORNITHIDAE (oilbird; 1 species)										
Steatornis caripensis. Oilbird			58	94*	16a*					S,U
NYCTIBIIDAE (potoos; 3 species)										
Nyctibius grandis. Great Potoo	89	62	65a*		92					A
Nyctibius griseus. Common Potoo	33	33		9			50			L
Nyctibius maculosus.(9) Andean Potoo			92							S
CAPRIMULGIDAE (nightjars; 17 species)										
Lurocalis semitorquatus.(10)										
Semicollared Nighthawk	89*			90						U,A,V
Chordeiles rupestris. Sand-colored Nighthawk		104	58	68*	16a*					A
Chordeiles acutipennis. Lesser Nighthawk		33								N
Nyctiprogne leucopyga. Band-tailed Nighthawk					2a*					N
Podager nacunda. Nacunda Nighthawk		33		9	104	94	9			L
Nyctidromus albicollis. Pauraque	33	9	9	9	9					L
Nyctiphrynus ocellatus. Ocellated Poorwill	33	76*	58		94					A,U
Caprimulgus rufus. Rufous Nightjar					9	9	26			V
Caprimulgus sericocaudatus. Silky-tailed Nightjar		103								F
Caprimulgus longirostris. Band-winged Nightjar			9	9	94					P/T,V
Caprimulgus maculicaudus. Spot-tailed Nightjar		9		9	94					N
Caprimulgus parvulus. Little Nightjar		9			9	94	9			L,V

	Pando	Beni	La Paz	Cochabamba	Santa Cruz	Chuquisaca	Tarija	Oruro	Potosí	life zone
Caprimulgus nigrescens. Blackish Nightjar		33								A
Hydropsalis climacocerca. Ladder-tailed Nightjar	89*		9	94	94					A
Hydropsalis brasiliana. Scissor-tailed Nightjar		33	9	9	94	94	26			L,V
Uropsalis segmentata. Swallow-tailed Nightjar			104	9						T,S
Uropsalis lyra. Lyre-tailed Nightjar			92	90				92		U,S

APODIDAE (swifts; 11 species)

	Pando	Beni	La Paz	Cochabamba	Santa Cruz	Chuquisaca	Tarija	Oruro	Potosí	life zone
Cypseloides fumigatus. Sooty Swift					60*		30			V
Cypseloides rutilus. Chestnut-collared Swift			94	9						H
Streptoprocne zonaris. White-collared Swift		76*	58	94	94	100*				L
Chaetura cinereiventris. Gray-rumped Swift	66		65a*							A
Chaetura egregia.(11) Pale-rumped Swift	66		65a*		111					A
Chaetura andrei. Ashy-tailed Swift					68*	92	92			N
Chaetura brachyura. Short-tailed Swift	66	75	65a*		68*					A
Aeronautes montivagus. White-tipped Swift			68*	85*	22					S
Aeronautes andecolus. Andean Swift			9	94	68*	134*	134*		9	V
Panyptila cayennensis. Lesser Swallow-tailed Swift	66*									A
Tachornis squamata. Fork-tailed Palm-Swift	89*	75*	65a*							A

TROCHILIDAE (hummingbirds; 74 species)

	Pando	Beni	La Paz	Cochabamba	Santa Cruz	Chuquisaca	Tarija	Oruro	Potosí	life zone
Doryfera ludoviciae. Green-fronted Lancebill			9	94						U
Glaucis hirsuta. Rufous-breasted Hermit	33	9	9	9	50					A
Threnetes leucurus. Pale-tailed Barbthroat	33	33	87	9	16a*					A
Phaethornis superciliosus. Long-tailed Hermit	89	58	9	9	121					A,U
Phaethornis hispidus. White-bearded Hermit	33	33	9	9	50					A
Phaethornis philippii. Needle-billed Hermit	66		65a*							A
Phaethornis pretrei. Planalto Hermit					121		9			F
Phaethornis subochraceus. Buff-bellied Hermit		91			9					N
Phaethornis nattereri. Cinnamon-throated Hermit					96					N
Phaethornis stuarti. White-browed Hermit		157	87	157	9					F
Phaethornis ruber. Reddish Hermit	33	9	9	104	2a					A
Eutoxeres condamini. Buff-tailed Sicklebill			14							U
Campylopterus largipennis. Gray-breasted Sabrewing		58	9	158	50					U,F
Eupetomena macroura. Swallow-tailed Hummingbird		33			121					N
Florisuga mellivora. White-necked Jacobin	33	9		9	50					A
Colibri delphinae. Brown Violetear			87		121					U
Colibri thalassinus. Green Violetear			9	9	94					S
Colibri coruscans. Sparkling Violetear		100	9	9	9	9	9		9	P/T,V
Colibri serrirostris. White-vented Violetear			9		9	9				V
Anthracothorax nigricollis. Black-throated Mango	33	9	9	9	121					A
Chrysolampis mosquitus. Ruby-topaz Hummingbird					96					N
Klais guimeti. Violet-headed Hummingbird			9	9	16a*					U
Lophornis gouldii. Dot-eared Coquette					96					N
Lophornis delattrei. Rufous-crested Coquette		(56)	9	9	50					F
Lophornis chalybea. Festive Coquette	33			9						A

	Pando	Beni	La Paz	Cochabamba	Santa Cruz	Chuquisaca	Tarija	Oruro	Potosi	life zone
Popelairia langsdorffi. Black-bellied Thorntail	66									A
Popelairia letitiae. Coppery Thorntail	no precise locality									A?
Chlorostilbon mellisugus. Blue-tailed Emerald	33	62	9		121					A
Chlorostilbon aureoventris. Glittering-bellied Emerald		104		9	9	9	9			N
Thalurania furcata. Fork-tailed Woodnymph	33	33	9	9	62	9				L,U
Hylocharis sapphirina. Rufous-throated Sapphire					96					N
Hylocharis cyanus. White-chinned Sapphire	89	158	94	158	9					A
Hylocharis chrysura. Gilded Hummingbird		9			62	94	9			N
Chrysuronia oenone. Golden-tailed Sapphire		158	9	158	50					U,F
Polytmus guainumbi. White-tailed Goldenthroat		104	94		121					N
Taphrospilus hypostictus. Many-spotted Hummingbird			104		121		(56)			U,F?
Amazilia chionogaster. White-bellied Hummingbird			9	9	9	9	9			V
Amazilia versicolor. Versicolored Emerald		9			96					N
Amazilia fimbriata. Glittering-throated Emerald		104		9						A
Amazilia lactea. Sapphire-spangled Emerald	33	9	9							A
Adelomyia melanogenys. Speckled Hummingbird			9	9	9	9	9			U
Polyplancta aurescens. Gould's Jewelfront	89	100		102						A
Heliodoxa leadbeateri. Violet-fronted Brilliant			9	9						U
Oreotrochilus estella. Andean Hillstar			9	9				9	9	P,P/T
Oreotrochilus leucopleurus. White-sided Hillstar							9			V
Oreotrochilus adela. Wedge-tailed Hillstar		104	9		159				9	V
Patagona gigas. Giant Hummingbird			9	9	104		94	100*	9	V
Aglaeactis pamela. Black-hooded Sunbeam			9	9						P/T
Pterophanes cyanoptera. Great Sapphirewing			9	9						P/T
Coeligena coeligena. Bronzy Inca			9	62	121	158				S
Coeligena torquata. Collared Inca		104	9	16a*						T,S
Coeligena violifer. Violet-throated Starfrontlet			9	9	94					T,P/T
Ensifera ensifera. Sword-billed Hummingbird			83*	121	68*					T/S
Heliangelus amethysticollis. Amethyst-throated Sunangel			9	9						T,S
Eriocnemis glaucopoides. Blue-capped Puffleg				9	104	9	94			T,S
Haplophaedia aureliae. Greenish Puffleg			9							U,S
Ocreatus underwoodii. Booted Racket-tail			9	62	121	160				U
Lesbia nuna. Green-tailed Trainbearer		104	100*							V
Sappho sparganura. Red-tailed Comet			9	9	121	9	9		9	V
Ramphomicron microrhynchum. Purple-backed Thornbill			102							T
Metallura aeneocauda. Scaled Metaltail			9	9						P/T
Metallura tyrianthina. Tyrian Metaltail			9	9	94					T,P/T
Chalcostigma ruficeps. Rufous-capped Thornbill			9	9						T,S
Chalcostigma olivaceum. Olivaceous Thornbill			9							P
Chalcostigma stanleyi. Blue-mantled Thornbill			9	121						P/T

	Pando	Beni	La Paz	Cochabamba	Santa Cruz	Chuquisaca	Tarija	Oruro	Potosí	life zone
Aglaiocercus kingi. Long-tailed Sylph			9	9	94					S,U
Schistes geoffroyi. Wedge-billed Hummingbird			86	121						U
Heliothryx aurita. Black-eared Fairy	89*	33	9		121					A
Heliactin cornuta. Horned Sungem					96					N
Heliomaster longirostris. Long-billed Starthroat	33	100	9	9	121					A
Heliomaster furcifer. Blue-tufted Starthroat			86*	9	50		9			N
Microstilbon burmeisteri. Slender-tailed Woodstar			163	94	121	9	9			V
Calliphlox amethystina. Amethyst Woodstar		84*	9		92					N
Acestrura mulsant. White-bellied Woodstar			104	9						T,S,P/
TROGONIDAE (trogons; 9 species)										
Pharomachrus antisianus. Crested Quetzal			58	122	9					U
Pharomachrus auriceps. Golden-headed Quetzal			58	9	94					S
Pharomachrus pavoninus. Pavonine Quetzal	89	33	65a*							A
Trogon melanurus. Black-tailed Trogon	33	33	9	9	50					A
Trogon viridis. White-tailed Trogon	33	33	65a*		2a					A
Trogon collaris. Collared Trogon	33	9	9		122					A
Trogon personatus. Masked Trogon			9	9	9					S,U
Trogon curucui. Blue-crowned Trogon	33	33	9	9	9		9			L,U
Trogon violaceus. Violaceous Trogon	33	76			2a‡					A
MOMOTIDAE (motmots; 3 species)										
Electron platyrhynchum. Broad-billed Motmot	89	100	87	9	94					A
Baryphthengus martii.(12) Rufous Motmot	89		9	94	94					A,U
Momotus momota. Blue-crowned Motmot	33	9	9	9	9	9	9			L
ALCEDINIDAE (kingfishers; 5 species)										
Ceryle torquata. Ringed Kingfisher	89*	9	58	94	104		9			L,V
Chloroceryle amazona. Amazon Kingfisher	33	58	58	94	104		52			L
Chloroceryle americana. Green Kingfisher	33	9	87	94	50		9			L
Chloroceryle inda. Green-and-rufous Kingfisher	33	9		9	94					A
Chloroceryle aenea. Pygmy Kingfisher	89	33		94	94					A
BUCCONIDAE (puffbirds; 14 species)										
Notharchus macrorhynchos. White-necked Puffbird	33	76*			123					A
Notharchus ordii. Brown-banded Puffbird	66									A
Notharchus tectus. Pied Puffbird					2a					A
Bucco macrodactylus. Chestnut-capped Puffbird	33	33		9						A
Nystalus chacuru. White-eared Puffbird		9	104		9					N
Nystalus striolatus. Striolated Puffbird	89		9	94	94					A
Nystalus maculatus. Spot-backed Puffbird				9	9	94	9			N,V
Malacoptila semicincta. Semicollared Puffbird	33		87							A
Malacoptila fulvogularis. Black-streaked Puffbird			9	62						U
Nonnula sclateri. Fulvous-chinned Nunlet	66									A
Nonnula ruficapilla. Gray-cheeked Nunlet	89		103		13a					A
Monasa nigrifrons. Black-fronted Nunbird	33	33	9	9	50					L
Monasa morphoeus. White-fronted Nunbird	33	9	9		2a					A
Chelidoptera tenebrosa. Swallow-wing	33	33	58		2a					A

	Pando	Beni	La Paz	Cochabamba	Santa Cruz	Chuquisaca	Tarija	Oruro	Potosí	life zone
GALBULIDAE (jacamars; 8 species)										
Galbalcyrhynchus purusianus.(13) Purus Jacamar	33	33								A
Brachygalba lugubris. Brown Jacamar					104					A
Brachygalba albogularis. White-throated Jacamar	66*		65a*							A
Galbula cyanescens. Bluish-fronted Jacamar	66		65a*							A
Galbula ruficauda. Rufous-tailed Jacamar	33	9	9	9	62					L
Galbula leucogastra.(14) Bronzy Jacamar	66									A
Galbula dea. Paradise Jacamar	89	33	65a*							A
Jacamerops aurea. Great Jacamar	33		65a*							A
CAPITONIDAE (barbets; 4 species)										
Capito dayi. Black-girdled Barbet					2a‡					A
Capito niger. Black-spotted Barbet	33	9	58	9	15					A
Eubucco richardsoni. Lemon-throated Barbet	89‡		103							A
Eubucco versicolor. Versicolored Barbet			9	9	16a*					U,S
RAMPHASTIDAE (toucans; 14 species)										
Aulacorhynchus prasinus. Emerald Toucanet	89	100	86*	64	64					A
Aulacorhynchus derbianus. Chestnut-tipped Toucanet		100	9	9						U
Aulacorhynchus coeruleicinctis. Blue-banded Toucanet			9	9	9					S
Pteroglossus inscriptus. Lettered Aracari	33	76*		94	2a					A
Pteroglossus bitorquatus. Red-necked Aracari					12					A
Pteroglossus flavirostris.(15) Ivory-billed Aracari	89	33	58	124						A
Pteroglossus castanotis. Chestnut-eared Aracari	33	33	9	9	9					A
Pteroglossus beauharnaesii. Curl-crested Aracari	33	1	65a*	94						A
Selenidera reinwardtii. Golden-collared Toucanet	66									A
Selenidera maculirostris. Spot-billed Toucanet					2a					A
Andigena cucullata. Hooded Mountain-Toucan			59	9						T
Ramphastos vitellinus.(16) Channel-billed Toucan	33	9	9	9	62					A,U
Ramphastos tucanus.(17) Red-billed Toucan	33	58	9	9	9					A
Ramphastos toco. Toco Toucan		9			9				9	N
PICIDAE (woodpeckers; 35 species)										
Picumnus rufiventris. Rufous-breasted Piculet	89	94		9						A
Picumnus fuscus.(18) Rusty-necked Piculet		108								N?
Picumnus minutissimus. Arrowhead Piculet	33	9	9	9	9					A,U
Picumnus aurifrons. Bar-breasted Piculet	89‡		108		2a					A
Picumnus cirratus.(19) White-barred Piculet			9	9	50	9	9			N,V
Melanerpes candidus. White Woodpecker		33			9	9	9	50		N
Melanerpes cruentatus. Yellow-tufted Woodpecker	33	33	9	9	9					A
Melanerpes cactorum. White-fronted Woodpecker					22	22	94	94		V
Picoides mixtus. Checkered Woodpecker						13a		50		N
Picoides lignarius. Striped Woodpecker				9	9	9	9		9	V
Veniliornis nigriceps. Bar-bellied Woodpecker			9	9	94					T,S
Veniliornis fumigatus. Smoky-brown Woodpecker			9	9	9			94		S,U
Veniliornis passerinus. Little Woodpecker	33	9	9	9	62			52		L,U

Species	Pando	Beni	La Paz	Cochabamba	Santa Cruz	Chuquisaca	Tarija	Oruro	Potosí	life zone
Veniliornis frontalis. Dot-fronted Woodpecker			58	9	9	9	9			V,S,N
Veniliornis affinis. Red-stained Woodpecker	33	33	9	9	94					A
Piculus flavigula. Yellow-throated Woodpecker					2a					A
Piculus leucolaemus. White-throated Woodpecker	89	33	9	9	125					A
Piculus chrysochloros. Golden-green Woodpecker	33	100	65a*		62		9			L
Piculus rubiginosus. Golden-olive Woodpecker			9	9	9	9	9			U,V
Piculus rivolii. Crimson-mantled Woodpecker			9	9						T,S
Colaptes punctigula. Spot-breasted Flicker	89	33	65a*	94	125					A
Colaptes melanochloros. Green-barred Flicker		62		9	130	130	9		9	V,N
Colaptes rupicola. Andean Flicker			9	9	94	9	60*	9	9	P,P/T
Colaptes campestris. Campo Flicker		9			9					N
Celeus grammicus. Scale-breasted Woodpecker	89	33	65a*							A
Celeus elegans. Chestnut Woodpecker	33	9								A
Celeus lugubris. Pale-crested Woodpecker		62			50					N
Celeus flavus. Cream-colored Woodpecker	33	33	65a*	9	125					A
Celeus spectabilis. Rufous-headed Woodpecker	89	9	87*	9						A
Celeus torquatus. Ringed Woodpecker	89		65a*		125					A
Dryocopus shulzi. Black-bodied Woodpecker						95	95			N
Dryocopus lineatus. Lineated Woodpecker	33	9	9	9	9	94	9			L
Campephilus melanoleucos. Crimson-crested Woodpecker	89	33	87*	85*	62	9				L
Campephilus rubricollis. Red-necked Woodpecker	33	33	9	9	9					A,U
Campephilus leucopogon. Cream-backed Woodpecker					94	22	98			V

DENDROCOLAPTIDAE (woodcreepers; 25 species)

Species	Pando	Beni	La Paz	Cochabamba	Santa Cruz	Chuquisaca	Tarija	Oruro	Potosí	life zone
Dendrocincla fuliginosa. Plain-brown Woodcreeper	33	33	8	33	33					A
Dendrocincla merula. White-chinned Woodcreeper	89	76	87		8					A
Deconychura longicauda. Long-tailed Woodcreeper	33	33	8							A
Sittasomus griseicapillus. Olivaceous Woodcreeper	33	8	8	8	8	163	8			L,V
Glyphorynchus spirurus. Wedge-billed Woodcreeper	33	33	87	8						A
Nasica longirostris. Long-billed Woodcreeper	33	33	65a*		2a*					A
Dendrexetastes rufigula. Cinnamon-throated Woodcreeper	33	33	87	8						A
Hylexetastes perrotii. Red-billed Woodcreeper					2a					A
Hylexetastes stresemanni. Bar-bellied Woodcreeper	66									A
Xiphocolaptes promeropirhynchus. Strong-billed Woodcreeper			8	8	8					S,F
Xiphocolaptes major. Great Rufous Woodcreeper		33	8	8	62	94	8			N,V
Dendrocolaptes certhia. Barred Woodcreeper	89	33	8	141	109					A
Dendrocolaptes concolor. Concolor Woodcreeper					2a					A
Dendrocolaptes picumnus. Black-banded Woodcreeper	89	33	8	8	8	8	8			L,U
Xiphorhynchus picus. Straight-billed Woodcreeper	33	8	65a*	8	8					A

	Pando	Beni	La Paz	Cochabamba	Santa Cruz	Chuquisaca	Tarija	Oruro	Potosí	33 life zone
Xiphorhynchus obsoletus. Striped Woodcreeper	33	33	65a*		2a					A
Xiphorhynchus ocellatus. Ocellated Woodcreeper		100	8	8	94					U,F
Xiphorhynchus spixii. Spix's Woodcreeper	33	33	8							A
Xiphorhynchus elegans. Elegant Woodcreeper					2a					A
Xiphorhynchus guttatus. Buff-throated Woodcreeper	33	33	8	8	62					A
Xiphorhynchus triangularis. Olive-backed Woodcreeper			8	8	8					U
Lepidocolaptes angustirostris. Narrow-billed Woodcreeper		8		8	8	94	8			N,V
Lepidocolaptes affinis. Spot-crowned Woodcreeper			8	8	8					H
Lepidocolaptes albolineatus. Lineated Woodcreeper	33		8	62	18					A
Campylorhamphus trochilirostris. Red-billed Scythebill	33	10	8	8	62					L
FURNARIIDAE (20) (ovenbirds; 86 species)										
Geositta rufipennis. Rufous-banded Miner			8	8				18	8	V
Geositta punensis. Puna Miner			59					18	8	P
Geositta cunicularia. Common Miner			8	94		60*		8	8	P
Geositta tenuirostris. Slender-billed Miner			8	8	8			8	8	P
Upucerthia dumetaria. Scale-throated Earthcreeper				94		100		8	8	P
Upucerthia jelskii. Plain-breasted Earthcreeper			8	8				8	8	P
Upucerthia andaecola. Rock Earthcreeper			8	8		8			8	V
Upucerthia ruficauda. Straight-billed Earthcreeper			18					8	8	P
Upucerthia harterti. Bolivian Earthcreeper				8	8	8				V
Cinclodes excelsior. Stout-billed Cinclodes			28a							P/T
Cinclodes fuscus. Bar-winged Cinclodes			8	8	94	22		8	8	P,P/T,V
Cinclodes atacamensis. White-winged Cinclodes			8	8			94	8	8	P
Furnarius rufus. Rufous Hornero		8	104	8	8	8	8			N,V
Furnarius leucopus. Pale-legged Hornero	33	8	87*	8	18					A
Furnarius cristatus. Crested Hornero						92	92			N
Phleocryptes melanops. Wren-like Rushbird			59	94	8			8		P
Leptasthenura andicola. Andean Tit-Spinetail			8							P/T,P
Leptasthenura aegithaloides. Plain-mantled Tit-Spinetail			8			94		8	8	V,P
Leptasthenura fuliginiceps. Brown-capped Tit-Spinetail			8	8	35	8	8		8	V,P/T
Leptasthenura yanacensis. Tawny Tit-Spinetail			8	8			60*		134	P/T
Schoeniophylax phryganophila. Chotoy Spinetail		8			50		98			N
Synallaxis azarae.(21) Azara's Spinetail			8	8	18	8	8	8		H,P/T
Synallaxis frontalis. Sooty-fronted Spinetail			8		8	8	8			N,V
Synallaxis cabanisi. Cabanis' Spinetail		94	86	8						U,F
Synallaxis hypospodia. Cinereous-breasted Spinetail		33			94					N
Synallaxis albescens. Pale-breasted Spinetail	89	8	65a*	8	94		8			L,V
Synallaxis gujanensis. Plain-crowned Spinetail	33	8	8	8	62					L

34

	Pando	Beni	La Paz	Cochabamba	Santa Cruz	Chuquisaca	Tarija	Oruro	Potosí	life zone
Synallaxis propinqua. White-bellied Spinetail	33	33								A
Synallaxis rutilans. Ruddy Spinetail	33	33	8		2a					A
Certhiaxis cinnamomea. Yellow-throated Spinetail	33	8		8	94		94			L
Poecilurus scutatus. Ochre-cheeked Spinetail					8	8	8			N,V
Cranioleuca pyrrhophia. Stripe-crowned Spinetail			8	8	8	8	8			V
Cranioleuca curtata. Ash-browed Spinetail			90*	90						U
Cranioleuca vulpina. Rusty-backed Spinetail	33	84		8						A
Cranioleuca albiceps. Light-crowned Spinetail			8	8	81					T
Cranioleuca gutturata. Speckled Spinetail	33		8	8						A
Schizoeaca harterti.(22) Black-throated Thistletail			8	8	80					P/T
Asthenes pyrrholeuca. Lesser Canastero							8			V
Asthenes dorbignyi. Creamy-breasted Canastero			8	8	59	8	8	8	8	V,P/T
Asthenes berlepschi.(23) Berlepsch's Canastero			34							P
Asthenes baeri. Short-billed Canastero								92		N
Asthenes modesta. Cordilleran Canastero			59	8				8	8	P
Asthenes pudibunda. Canyon Canastero			8	8						P,V
Asthenes anthoides. Austral Canastero			8	8					8	P
Asthenes humilis. Streak-throated Canastero			8							P
Asthenes maculicauda. Scribble-tailed Canastero			8	8						P/T
Asthenes urubambensis. Line-fronted Canastero			8	94						P/T
Thripophaga fusciceps. Plain Softtail		100	65a*	8						A
Phacellodomus rufifrons. Rufous-fronted Thornbird		8			8		8			N
Phacellodomus striaticeps. Streak-fronted Thornbird			8	8	94	8		8	8	V,P
Phacellodomus ruber. Greater Thornbird		8			18					N
Phacellodomus striaticollis.										
Freckle-breasted Thornbird				78	8	8	8			V
Coryphistera alaudina. Lark-like Brushrunner					110	50	26			N
Metopothrix aurantiacus.										
Orange-fronted Plushcrown		33								A
Margarornis squamiger. Pearled Treerunner			8	8	94					T,S
Premnoplex brunnescens. Spotted Barbtail			8	8						U
Pseudocolaptes boissonneautii.										
Streaked Tuftedcheek			59	8	68*					T,S
Berlepschia rikeri. Point-tailed Palmcreeper	66									A
Pseudoseisura cristata. Rufous Cachalote		33			50					N
Pseudoseisura lophotes. Brown Cachalote					69		26			N
Hyloctistes subulatus. Striped Woodhaunter	89	100	103							A
Ancistrops strigilatus. Chestnut-winged Hookbill	89		103							A
Syndactyla rufosuperciliata.										
Buff-browed Foliage-gleaner			8	62	8	8	8			U,S
Simoxenops ucayalae. Peruvian Recurvebill	66									A
Simoxenops striatus. Bolivian Recurvebill			8	8						F
Anabacerthia striaticollis. Montane Foliage-gleaner			8	8						U
Philydor erythrocercus.(24)										
Rufous-rumped Foliage-gleaner	33	33	8	8						U,A

	Pando	Beni	La Paz	Cochabamba	Santa Cruz	Chuquisaca	Tarija	Oruro	Potosí	life zone
Philydor pyrrhodes.										
Cinnamon-rumped Foliage-gleaner	33	75								A
Philydor rufus. Buff-fronted Foliage-gleaner	89*		8		3	94				U,A
Philydor erythropterus.										
Chestnut-winged Foliage-gleaner	89	33	65a							A
Philydor ruficaudatus.										
Rufous-tailed Foliage-gleaner	33	33	8	59						A
Automolus infuscatus.										
Olive-backed Foliage-gleaner	66									A
Automolus rubiginosus. Ruddy Foliage-gleaner			4							A
Automolus ochrolaemus.										
Buff-throated Foliage-gleaner	33	59	8	8	94					A,U
Automolus rufipileatus.										
Chestnut-crowned Foliage-gleaner	33	(56)	8	8						A
Automolus melanopezus.										
Brown-rumped Foliage-gleaner	66									A
Thripadectes holostictus. Striped Treehunter			8	8						U,S
Thripadectes scrutator. Buff-throated Treehunter				90						T
Xenops tenuirostris. Slender-billed Xenops	33									A
Xenops rutilans. Streaked Xenops	89	33	8	8	62	8	8			L,U
Xenops minutus. Plain Xenops	33	33	8	8	94					A
Sclerurus albigularis. Gray-throated Leafscraper		100	8		94					F
Sclerurus mexicanus. Tawny-throated Leafscraper	89	100	87	8	94					A
Sclerurus rufigularis. Short-billed Leafscraper		33			2a					A
Sclerurus caudacutus. Black-tailed Leafscraper	33									A
Lochmias nematura. Sharp-tailed Streamcreeper			8	59	8	8	94			U
FORMICARIIDAE (antbirds; 87 species)										
Cymbilaimus lineatus. Fasciated Antshrike	89*		8							A
Cymbilaimus sanctaemariae.(25) Bamboo Antshrike	33		65a*							A
Batara cinerea. Giant Antshrike					8	94	8			S,U
Taraba major. Great Antshrike	33	8	8	8	62	94	26			L
Thamnophilus doliatus. Barred Antshrike	33	8	59	8	8		8			L
Thamnophilus palliatus. Lined Antshrike		8	8	8	140					F
Thamnophilus aethiops.										
White-shouldered Antshrike	89	8	87	8	2a					A
Thamnophilus schistaceus. Black-capped Antshrike	33	8	8	8	50					A
Thamnophilus aroyae. Upland Antshrike			88	8						U
Thamnophilus punctatus. Slaty Antshrike		62		8	8					N
Thamnophilus amazonicus. Amazonian Antshrike	33	33			2a					A
Thamnophilus caerulescens. Variable Antshrike			8	8	8	8	8			W
Thamnophilus ruficapillus.										
Rufous-capped Antshrike			8	8	8	8	8			S,V
Thamnophilus torquatus. Rufous-winged Antshrike					35					N
Pygiptila stellaris. Spot-winged Antshrike	33	33	65a*		2a					A
Thamnistes anabatinus. Russet Antshrike				8						F

	Pando	Beni	La Paz	Cochabamba	Santa Cruz	Chuquisaca	Tarija	Oruro	Potosi	life zone
Dysithamnus mentalis. Plain Antvireo			59	8	139					U,F
Thamnomanes ardesiacus.										
Dusky-throated Antshrike	66									A
Thamnomanes saturninus. Saturnine Antshrike					2a					A
Thamnomanes schistogynus. Bluish-slate Antshrike	33		8	8						A
Myrmotherula brachyura. Pygmy Antwren	33	33	59	8	94					A
Myrmotherula sclateri. Sclater's Antwren	66		65a*							A
Myrmotherula surinamensis. Streaked Antwren	66*		65a*		2a					A
Myrmotherula longicauda. Stripe-chested Antwren			59	8						F
Myrmotherula hauxwelli. Plain-throated Antwren	33	8			2a					A
Myrmotherula leucophthalma. White-eyed Antwren	89		8		2a					A
Myrmotherula haematonota.										
Stipple-throated Antwren	66									A
Myrmotherula ornata. Ornate Antwren	33		8	59						A
Myrmotherula axillaris. White-flanked Antwren	33	8	8	8	94					A
Myrmotherula longipennis. Long-winged Antwren	66									A
Myrmotherula grisea. Ashy Antwren			8	88	88					F
Myrmotherula menetriesii. Gray Antwren	33	33	8	8	94					A
Myrmotherula assimilis. Leaden Antwren	33	163								A
Dichrozona cincta. Banded Antbird	89	33	8							A
Myrmorchilus strigilatus. Stripe-backed Antbird					8		8			N
Herpsilochmus pileatus. Black-capped Antwren					8	8	8			N
Herpsilochmus longirostris. Large-billed Antwren		20								N
Herpsilochmus rufimarginatus.										
Rufous-winged Antwren		33	8		94					F
Microrhopias quixensis. Dot-winged Antwren	89	1								A
Formicivora grisea. White-fringed Antwren					12					N
Formicivora melanogaster. Black-bellied Antwren					50	94	8			N
Formicivora rufa. Rusty-backed Antwren		8		8	35					N
Drymophila devillei. Striated Antbird	33		8	137						A
Drymophila caudata. Long-tailed Antbird			8							S
Terenura humeralis. Chestnut-shouldered Antwren	66									A
Terenura sharpei. Yellow-rumped Antwren			88	17						U
Cercomacra cinerascens. Gray Antbird	33	33	8		2a					A
Cercomacra nigrescens. Blackish Antbird	33	1	136	136	2a					A
Cercomacra serva. Black Antbird	89	1	8							A
Cercomacra sp. nov.(26)	66									A
Cercomacra melanaria. Mato Grosso Antbird		33		8	94					N
Pyriglena leuconota. White-backed Fire-eye		62	8	8	8					U,N
Myrmoborus leucophrys. White-browed Antbird	33	8	8	8	94					A
Myrmoborus myotherinus. Black-faced Antbird	89	33	8	8	138					A
Hypocnemis cantator. Warbling Antbird	33	33	8	8	2a					A
Hypocnemoides maculicauda. Band-tailed Antbird	33	33	94	8	94					A
Myrmochanes hemileucus. Black-and-white Antbird		1								A
Sclateria naevia. Silvered Antbird	33	33			2a					A

	Pando	Beni	La Paz	Cochabamba	Santa Cruz	Chuquisaca	Tarija	Oruro	Potosí	life zone
Percnostola leucostigma. Spot-winged Antbird	66									A
Percnostola lophotes. White-lined Antbird	66		65a*							A
Myrmeciza hemimelaena. Chestnut-tailed Antbird	33	8	8	8	94					A,U
Myrmeciza hyperythra. Plumbeous Antbird	33	8	65a*							A
Myrmeciza goeldii. Goeldi's Antbird	66									A
Myrmeciza fortis. Sooty Antbird	66									A
Myrmeciza atrothorax. Black-throated Antbird	33	8	8	8	8					A
Gymnopithys salvini. White-throated Antbird	33	33	65a*143							A
Rhegmatorhina melanosticta. Hairy-crested Antbird	89	100	6							A
Hylophylax naevia. Spot-backed Antbird	89	33	8	8	78					A
Hylophylax punctulata. Dot-backed Antbird	33	75								A
Hylophylax poecilinota. Scale-backed Antbird	89	33	87		2a					A
Phlegopsis nigromaculata. Black-spotted Bare-eye	33	8	59	8	35					A
Phlegopsis erythroptera. Reddish-winged Bare-eye	66									A
Formicarius colma. Rufous-capped Antthrush	66		65a*		2a					A
Formicarius analis. Black-faced Antthrush	33	8	8	8	35					A
Chamaeza nobilis. Striated Antthrush	66									A
Chamaeza campanisona. Short-tailed Antthrush			8	8	8					U
Chamaeza mollissima. Barred Antthrush			8	8						T,S
Grallaria squamigera. Undulated Antpitta			8	8						T
Grallaria guatimalensis. Scaled Antpitta			14	68*						U
Grallaria albigula. White-throated Antpitta				68‡	8					U
Grallaria rufula. Rufous Antpitta			83	8						T
Grallaria erythrotis. Rufous-faced Antpitta			8	8	68*					T,S
Hylopezus macularius. Spotted Antpitta	33									A
Hylopezus berlepschi. Amazonian Antpitta		33	87	8	94					A
Myrmothera campanisona. Thrush-like Antpitta	66									A
Grallaricula flavirostris. Ochre-breasted Antpitta			8	8						S
Grallaricula ferrugineipectus. Rusty-breasted Antpitta			103							T
CONOPOPHAGIDAE (gnateaters; 2 species)										
Conopophaga ardesiaca. Slaty Gnateater			8	8	82	8	94			U
Conopophaga melanogaster. Black-bellied Gnateater		1								A
RHINOCRYPTIDAE (tapaculos; 7 species)										
Rhinocrypta lanceolata. Crested Gallito					56					N
Melanopareia torquata. Collared Crescentchest					35					N
Melanopareia maximiliani. Olive-crowned Crescentchest			8	94	8	8	94			V
Scytalopus unicolor. Unicolored Tapaculo			148	68‡	68‡					T,S
Scytalopus femoralis. Rufous-vented Tapaculo			8	68‡	94					U
Scytalopus magellanicus. Andean Tapaculo			8	8						T,P/T
Scytalopus superciliaris. White-browed Tapaculo						8	60*			S
TYRANNIDAE (27) (tyrant flycatchers; 197 species)										
Phyllomyias fasciatus. Planalto Tyrannulet					12					N
Phyllomyias burmeisteri. Rough-legged Tyrannulet				8	95					U

	Pando	Beni	La Paz	Cochabamba	Santa Cruz	Chuquisaca	Tarija	Oruro	Potosí	life zone
Phyllomyias sclateri. Sclater's Tyrannulet			28	8	8	8	8			U
Phyllomyias uropygialis.										
Tawny-rumped Tyrannulet			8	8	95	8	95			T,S,P/
Zimmerius bolivianus. Bolivian Tyrannulet			8	8						S,U
Zimmerius gracilipes. Slender-footed Tyrannulet	89	151	8	8	2a					A
Ornithion inerme. White-lored Tyrannulet	66		65a*		2a‡					A
Camptostoma obsoletum.										
Southern Beardless Tyrannulet	33	8	8	8	8	8	8			L,V
Phaeomyias murina. Mouse-colored Tyrannulet	33	8	37	8	8	8	8			L,V
Sublegatus modestus. Scrub Flycatcher	89	33	131	8	62	8	8			L,V
Suiriri suiriri. Suiriri Flycatcher		33		8	62	95	8			N,V
Tyrannulus elatus. Yellow-crowned Flycatcher	33	8	87	85*						A
Myiopagis gaimardii. Forest Elaenia	33	33	8	36	101					A
Myiopagis caniceps. Gray Elaenia	89‡		87	68*	101		8			L
Myiopagis viridicata. Greenish Elaenia	33	33	59		8	8	50			L
Elaenia flavogaster. Yellow-bellied Elaenia		8	8	8	95	8				N
Elaenia spectabilis. Large Elaenia	89	8	87		8		8			L,V
Elaenia albiceps. White-crested Elaenia			8	131	8	131	131			T,S,P/.
Elaenia parvirostris. Small-billed Elaenia	33	8	65a*	8	8	8	8			L,V
Elaenia strepera. Slaty Elaenia				95	8	8	95			S
Elaenia gigas. Mottle-backed Elaenia			8		95					F
Elaenia pelzelni. Brownish Elaenia	33									A
Elaenia chiriquensis. Lesser Elaenia		8	8		95					N
Elaenia obscura. Highland Elaenia			8	8	8	8	8			S,U
Elaenia pallatangae. Sierran Elaenia			83	128						T,S
Mecocerculus leucophrys.										
White-throated Tyrannulet			8	8	8	8	95			T,S,P/
Mecocerculus hellmayri. Buff-banded Tyrannulet			86	8	8	8	82			U
Mecocerculus stictopterus.										
White-banded Tyrannulet			83	8						T
Serpophaga cinerea. Torrent Tyrannulet			59	8						S,U,F
Serpophaga hypoleuca. River Tyrannulet	33									A
Serpophaga nigricans. Sooty Tyrannulet							8			N
Serpophaga munda.(28) White-bellied Tyrannulet			59	8	8	8	8		8	N,V
Serpophaga subcristata. White-crested Tyrannulet			86‡	8	8	95	8			N
Inezia inornata. Plain Tyrannulet	33	8	65a*	8	72		8			L
Inezia subflava. Pale-tipped Tyrannulet		95			2a					A
Stigmatura budytoides. Greater Wagtail-Tyrant					8	8	8			V
Anairetes alpinus. Ash-breasted Tit-Tyrant			8							P/T
Anairetes flavirostris. Yellow-billed Tit-Tyrant			104	8	8	8	8	8	8	V,P
Anairetes parulus. Tufted Tit-Tyrant			8	8				8	8	P/T,V
Tachuris rubrigastra. Many-colored Rush-Tyrant			59					8		P
Culicivora caudacuta. Sharp-tailed Tyrant		100			37					N
Polystictus pectoralis. Bearded Tachuri					36					N
Pseudocolopteryx sclateri. Crested Doradito			33							N

	Pando	Beni	La Paz	Cochabamba	Santa Cruz	Chuquisaca	Tarija	Oruro	Potosí	life zone
Pseudocolopteryx dinellianus. Dinelli's Doradito							51			N
Pseudocolopteryx acutipennis. Subtropical Doradito		100	8	8	95	8	95		8	W
Pseudocolopteryx flaviventris. Warbling Doradito					95					L
Euscarthmus melacoryphus.										
Tawny-crowned Pygmy-Tyrant	89‡	8			95		8			L
Mionectes striaticollis. Streak-necked Flycatcher			8	8	95					H
Mionectes oleagineus. Ochre-bellied Flycatcher	89	33	59	8	114					A
Mionectes macconnelli. McConnell's Flycatcher	89	8	8	95	8					U,A
Leptopogon amaurocephalus.										
Sepia-capped Flycatcher	33	8	8	33	62	95	8			L
Leptopogon superciliaris. Slaty-capped Flycatcher		100	8	8	95					U
Phylloscartes ophthalmicus.										
Marble-faced Bristle-Tyrant			8	8						U
Phylloscartes orbitalis. Spectacled Bristle-Tyrant		100	87	8						F
Phylloscartes flaveolus. Yellow Tyrannulet	89				36					A
Phylloscartes ventralis. Mottle-cheeked Tyrannulet			8	8	8	8	8			U,S
Corythopis torquata. Ringed Antpipit	33	33	8	35	116					A
Corythopis delalandi. Southern Antpipit					35					N
Pseudotriccus simplex.										
Hazel-fronted Pygmy-Tyrant			8	59						U
Pseudotriccus ruficeps.										
Rufous-headed Pygmy-Tyrant			59	95						T
Myiornis albiventris.										
White-breasted Pygmy-Tyrant			8	8	95					F
Myiornis ecaudatus.										
Short-tailed Pygmy-Tyrant	33	8	8	8	50					A
Lophotriccus eulophotes.										
Long-crested Pygmy-Tyrant	66									A
Hemitriccus minor. Snethlage's Tody-Tyrant					2a					A
Hemitriccus flammulatus.										
Flammulated Tody-Tyrant	33	33	8	8	110					A
Hemitriccus zosterops. White-eyed Tody-Tyrant	89	8	8		95					A
Hemitriccus iohannis. Johannis' Tody-Tyrant	33	33	65a							A
Hemitriccus striaticollis.										
Stripe-necked Tody-Tyrant	33	33	87		2a					A
Hemitriccus spodiops. Yungas Tody-Tyrant			88	8						U
Hemitriccus margaritaceiventer.										
Pearly-vented Tody-Tyrant		33	8	8	8	8	8			N,V
Hemitriccus granadensis.										
Black-throated Tody-Tyrant			67							S
Hemitriccus rufigularis. Buff-throated Tody-Tyrant		100	8		95					U
Todirostrum plumbeiceps.										
Ochre-faced Tody-Flycatcher			8	150	95	8	8			S,U
Todirostrum latirostre.										
Rusty-fronted Tody-flycatcher	33	33	8	8	50					L

	Pando	Beni	La Paz	Cochabamba	Santa Cruz	Chuquisaca	Tarija	Oruro	Potosí	life zone
Todirostrum maculatum. Spotted Tody-Flycatcher	33	33	65a							A
Todirostrum cinereum. Common Tody-Flycatcher		8			95					N
Todirostrum chrysocrotaphum. Golden-browed Tody-Flycatcher	33	33	8	8	95					A
Cnipodectes subbrunneus. Brownish Flycatcher	66									A
Ramphotrigon megacephala. Large-headed Flatbill	33		8	149	95					A
Ramphotrigon fuscicauda. Dusky-tailed Flatbill	33	65								A
Ramphotrigon ruficauda. Rufous-tailed Flatbill	33	33	65a		2a					A
Rhynchocyclus olivaceus. Olivaceous Flatbill			87	8						F
Rhynchocyclus fulvipectus. Fulvous-breasted Flatbill			86	149						U
Tolmomyias sulphurescens. Yellow-olive Flycatcher	33	8	8	8	62	95	8			L,V
Tolmomyias assimilis. Yellow-margined Flycatcher	33	33	8	8	2a					A
Tolmomyias poliocephalus. Gray-crowned Flycatcher	33		65a							A
Tolmomyias flaviventris. Yellow-breasted Flycatcher	89	33	8							A
Platyrinchus mystaceus. White-throated Spadebill		100	59	8	107					U,N
Platyrinchus coronatus. Golden-crowned Spadebill	33	33	87							A
Platyrinchus platyrhynchos. White-crested Spadebill	33		8							A
Onychorhynchus coronatus. Royal Flycatcher	33	8	8	22	2a					A
Terenotriccus erythrurus. Ruddy-tailed Flycatcher	33	33	8	8	95					A
Myiobius villosus. Tawny-breasted Flycatcher			104							U
Myiophobus inornatus. Unadorned Flycatcher			8	8						U
Myiophobus ochraceiventris. Ochraceous-breasted Flycatcher			59							T
Myiophobus fasciatus. Bran-colored Flycatcher	89	8	8	8	8	8	8			L,V
Pyrrhomyias cinnamomea. Cinnamon Flycatcher			8	8	8	8	95			S,U
Mitrephanes olivaceus. Olive Flycatcher			37	62						U
Contopus borealis. Olive-sided Flycatcher (N)			59		85*	101				V,U
Contopus fumigatus. Greater Pewee			8	8	147	8	8			S,U
Contopus virens. Eastern Wood-Pewee (N)		95								A
Contopus sordidulus. Western Wood-Pewee (N)		33?	8	95						U,S
Contopus cinereus. Tropical Pewee			8	8	8		8			F,V
Empidonax alnorum. Alder Flycatcher (N)	33	33		33	95	95				L
Lathrotriccus euleri.(29) Euler's Flycatcher	33	8	8	8	8	8	8			L,U
Cnemotriccus fuscatus. Fuscous Flycatcher	33	3	36	95	62	95	8			L
Sayornis nigricans. Black Phoebe		100*	8	59	8	8	8			U,F
Pyrocephalus rubinus. Vermilion Flycatcher	33	8	8	8	50	95	8			L
Ochthoeca cinnamomeiventris. Slaty-backed Chat-Tyrant			8	8	68*					S
Ochthoeca frontalis. Crowned Chat-Tyrant			8	8	132					T
Ochthoeca pulchella. Golden-browed Chat-Tyrant				8	132	132				S

	Pando	Beni	La Paz	Cochabamba	Santa Cruz	Chuquisaca	Tarija	Oruro	Potosi	life zone
Ochthoeca rufipectoralis.										
Rufous-breasted Chat-Tyrant			8	8	95					P/T,T
Ochthoeca fumicolor. Brown-backed Chat-Tyrant			8	8						P/T
Ochthoeca oenanthoides. D'Orbigny's Chat-Tyrant			8	8		95		8	8	V,P/T
Ochthoeca leucophrys. White-browed Chat-Tyrant			8	8	144	8			8	P/T
Ochthornis littoralis.(30) Drab Water-Tyrant	89*	8	8	85*						A
Myiotheretes striaticollis.										
Streak-throated Bush-Tyrant			59	8	8		8			U,S
Myiotheretes erythropygius.										
Red-rumped Bush-Tyrant			8	95						P/T
Myiotheretes rufipennis.										
Rufous-webbed Bush-Tyrant			8	8				134	8	P/T,P
Myiotheretes fuscorufus. Rufous-bellied Bush-Tyrant			59	8						T
Xolmis cinerea. Gray Monjita		33			62		98			N
Xolmis coronata. Black-crowned Monjita					37	95	50			N
Xolmis velata. White-rumped Monjita		8			50					N
Xolmis irupero. White Monjita		33			8	95	8			N
Agriornis montana. Black-billed Shrike-Tyrant			8	8		8	95	100	8	P
Agriornis andicola. White-tailed Shrike-Tyrant		59								P
Agriornis microptera. Gray-bellied Shrike-Tyrant		59	8				8	8	8	P,V
Agriornis murina. Mouse-brown Shrike-Tyrant				95	37	95	8			V,N
Muscisaxicola maculirostris.										
Spot-billed Ground-Tyrant			8	8	95		8	95	8	P,V
Muscisaxicola fluviatilis. Little Ground-Tyrant	89*		8	8	101*					A
Muscisaxicola capistrata.										
Cinnamon-bellied Ground-Tyrant			59	95				8	8	P
Muscisaxicola rufivertex.										
Rufous-naped Ground-Tyrant			8	8				8	8	P
Muscisaxicola juninensis. Puna Ground-Tyrant			8					100	8	P
Muscisaxicola albilora.										
White-browed Ground-Tyrant			8	8						P
Muscisaxicola alpina. Plain-capped Ground-Tyrant			8	8						P,P/T
Muscisaxicola cinerea. Cinereous Ground-Tyrant			8	8		8		95	8	P
Muscisaxicola albifrons.										
White-fronted Ground-Tyrant			8							P
Muscisaxicola flavinucha.										
Ochre-naped Ground-Tyrant			8	8				100	8	P,V
Muscisaxicola frontalis.										
Black-fronted Ground-Tyrant		95						8	8	P
Lessonia oreas. Andean Rufous-backed Negrito		59	95				5	59	8	P
Lessonia rufa. Southern Rufous-backed Negrito					95		8			V
Knipolegus striaticeps. Cinereous Tyrant					36	95	8			N
Knipolegus hudsoni. Hudson's Black-Tyrant		33	95		95					N
Knipolegus signatus. Plumbeous Tyrant				62	8	8	8			U
Knipolegus poecilurus. Rufous-tailed Tyrant					145					S

	Pando	Beni	La Paz	Cochabamba	Santa Cruz	Chuquisaca	Tarija	Oruro	Potosí	life zone
Knipolegus aterrimus. White-winged Black-Tyrant			8	8	8	8	8		8	W
Hymenops perspicillata. Spectacled Tyrant		8		59	50	95	8			N
Fluvicola pica. Pied Water-Tyrant	33	33	65a*	8	8	95	8			L
Fluvicola leucocephala. White-headed Marsh-Tyrant		8			36					L
Colonia colonus. Long-tailed Tyrant	33	1	144	8						A
Alectrurus tricolor. Cock-tailed Tyrant		36			36					N
Gubernetes yetapa. Streamer-tailed Tyrant		8			36					N
Satrapa icterophrys. Yellow-browed Tyrant	89*	8	87	8	50	8	8			L,V
Hirundinea ferruginea.(31) Cliff Flycatcher			8	8	59	8	95	8		V
Machetornis rixosus. Cattle Tyrant		8			36		8			N
Attila cinnamomeus. Cinnamon Attila	33	76								A
Attila bolivianus. Dull-capped Attila	33	8		8	36					A
Attila spadiceus. Bright-rumped Attila	89		87	8	38					A
Casiornis rufa. Rufous Casiornis	33	33	59	8	8	8	8			L,V
Rhytipterna simplex. Grayish Mourner	33	33	8	142	142					A
Laniocera hypopyrra. Cinereous Mourner	33	8	87	59	95					A
Sirystes sibilator. Sirystes	89	62	8	8	61					L
Myiarchus tuberculifer. Dusky-capped Flycatcher	33	33	8	8	8	8	8			A,U,S
Myiarchus swainsoni. Swainson's Flycatcher	89	8	8	8	8	49	8			L
Myiarchus ferox. Short-crested Flycatcher	33	8	8	8	8	8				A
Myiarchus cephalotes. Pale-edged Flycatcher			8	59	49					U
Myiarchus tyrannulus. Brown-crested Flycatcher	33	8	8	8	62	8	8			L,V
Pitangus lictor.(32) Lesser Kiskadee	33	8	87	8	95					L
Pitangus sulphuratus. Great Kiskadee	33	8	59	8	8	36	8		8	L,V
Megarhynchus pitangua. Boat-billed Flycatcher	33	8	59	8	50					L
Myiozetetes cayanensis. Rusty-margined Flycatcher	33	8	65a*	95	36					A
Myiozetetes similis. Social Flycatcher	33	33	8	8	50					A
Myiozetetes granadensis. Gray-capped Flycatcher	89*	33	8	146	95					A
Myiozetetes luteiventris. Dusky-chested Flycatcher	66		65a*							A
Conopias trivirgata. Three-striped Flycatcher				90						A
Myiodynastes chrysocephalus. Golden-crowned Flycatcher			8	8	95	8	95			U
Myiodynastes maculatus. Streaked Flycatcher	33	8	8	8	8	8	8			L,V
Myiodynastes luteiventris. Sulphur-bellied Flycatcher (N)		33		146	146					A
Legatus leucophaius. Piratic Flycatcher	33	8	8	8	36					L
Empidonomus varius. Variegated Flycatcher		33	59		8	8	8			L,V
Empidonomus aurantioatrocristatus.(33) Crowned Slaty-Flycatcher	89	33	8	59	8	8	8			L,V
Tyrannopsis sulphurea. Sulphury Flycatcher	66‡									A
Tyrannus albogularis. White-throated Kingbird		33			19a					N

	Pando	Beni	La Paz	Cochabamba	Santa Cruz	Chuquisaca	Tarija	Oruro	Potosí	life zone
Tyrannus melancholicus. Tropical Kingbird	33	33	8	8	8		8			L,V
Tyrannus savana. Fork-tailed Flycatcher	33	8	59	145	36	95	8			L
Tyrannus tyrannus. Eastern Kingbird (N)		8		85*	36		8			L
Xenopsaris albinucha. White-naped Xenopsaris		33			95					N
Pachyramphus viridis. Green-backed Becard					50	95	8			N,F
Pachyramphus versicolor. Barred Becard				8						S
Pachyramphus castaneus. Chestnut-crowned Becard	89‡		59	59						A
Pachyramphus polychopterus. White-winged Becard	33	33	8	8	8	8	2			L
Pachyramphus marginatus. Black-capped Becard	33	33	8	59						A
Pachyramphus minor. Pink-throated Becard	33	33	8	36	36					A
Pachyramphus validus. Crested Becard			8	8	8	8	8			L,U
Tityra cayana. Black-tailed Tityra	33	8			8					A
Tityra semifasciata. Masked Tityra	33	33	8	8	36					A,U
Tityra inquisitor. Black-crowned Tityra	33	33	87*	8	59					A
COTINGIDAE (cotingas; 17 species)										
Laniisoma elegans. Shrike-like Cotinga			8							U
Phibalura flavirostris. Swallow-tailed Cotinga			8							U
Ampelion rubrocristatus. Red-crested Cotinga			8	8						P/T,T
Ampelion rufaxilla. Chestnut-crested Cotinga			59							S
Pipreola intermedia. Band-tailed Fruiteater			8	8						S,T
Pipreola arcuata. Barred Fruiteater			8	8						T,S
Pipreola frontalis. Scarlet-breasted Fruiteater			59	8	8					U
Ampelioides tschudii. Scaled Fruiteater			67							U
Iodopleura isabellae. White-browed Purpletuft	33									A
Lipaugus vociferans. Screaming Piha	33	33	8	59	127					A
Lipaugus uropygialis.(34) Scimitar-winged Piha			8	59						S
Cotinga maynana. Plum-throated Cotinga		33	65a*							A
Cotinga cayana. Spangled Cotinga	89	1	87	22						A
Gymnoderus foetidus. Bare-necked Fruitcrow	33	33	65a*	8	95					A
Querula purpurata. Purple-throated Fruitcrow	33	8								A
Cephalopterus ornatus. Amazonian Umbrellabird	33	76*	8	8	95					A
Rupicola peruviana. Andean Cock-of-the-Rock			8	8						U
PHYTOTOMIDAE (plantcutters; 1 species)										
Phytotoma rutila. White-tipped Plantcutter			8	22	8	36	8		8	V
PIPRIDAE (manakins; 15 species)										
Schiffornis major. Greater Manakin	33	76								A
Schiffornis turdinus. Thrush-like Manakin	89	33	8	8	8					A,U
Piprites chloris. Wing-barred Manakin	33	33	8	38	95					A
Tyranneutes stolzmanni. Dwarf Tyrant-Manakin	33	55	87							A
Neopelma sulphureiventer. Sulphur-bellied Tyrant-Manakin	33	33	8	8	91					A
Heterocercus linteatus. Flame-crowned Manakin					2a					A

	Pando	Beni	La Paz	Cochabamba	Santa Cruz	Chuquisaca	Tarija	Oruro	Potosí	life zone
Machaeropterus pyrocephalus.										
Fiery-capped Manakin	33	56	95		2a					A
Manacus manacus. White-bearded Manakin	89	56			2a					A
Chiroxiphia pareola. Blue-backed Manakin	89				2a					A
Chiroxiphia boliviana.(35) Yungas Manakin				8	8	8	95			U
Pipra coronata. Blue-crowned Manakin	89	100	87	8						A
Pipra nattereri. Snow-capped Manakin					2a					A
Pipra fasciicauda. Band-tailed Manakin	33	33	59	8	50					L
Pipra rubrocapilla. Red-headed Manakin	33	33			2a					A
Pipra chloromeros. Round-tailed Manakin	89	59	8	8	50					A
HIRUNDINIDAE (swallows; 18 species)										
Tachycineta albiventer. White-winged Swallow	33	59	95	8	2a					A
Tachycineta leucorrhoa. White-rumped Swallow		8			95		8			N
Tachycineta leucopyga. Chilean Swallow			103		101*					L
Progne tapera. Brown-chested Martin	89‡	8	59	95	8	95	26			L
Progne subis. Purple Martin (N)	33	76*		95		95				L,V
Progne chalybea. Gray-breasted Martin	89	76*		104	59		98			L
Progne modesta. Southern Martin				40	40		8			N
Notiochelidon murina. Brown-bellied Swallow			8	95						P/T,T
Notiochelidon cyanoleuca. Blue-and-white Swallow	89*		59	8	62		8	8	8	W
Notiochelidon flavipes. Pale-footed Swallow			67*	68*	68*					T
Atticora fasciata. White-banded Swallow	89*	33	8		2a					A
Neochelidon tibialis. White-thighed Swallow	66									A
Alopochelidon fucata. Tawny-headed Swallow				8	95		98			N
Stelgidopteryx ruficollis.(36)										
Southern Rough-winged Swallow	89*	8	104	8	8		8			L
Riparia riparia. Bank Swallow (N)		76a		24*	162			68*		W
Hirundo rustica. Barn Swallow (N)		33		95	101			100*	8	W
Hirundo andecola. Andean Swallow				8	8		8	8	8	P,P/T
Hirundo pyrrhonota. Cliff Swallow (N)		76*		68*	68*	92		68*		W
TROGLODYTIDAE (wrens; 13 species)										
Campylorhynchus turdinus. Thrush-like Wren	33	8	59	8	50					L
Odontorchilus branickii. Gray-mantled Wren			67*							U
Cinnycerthia peruana. Sepia-brown Wren			8	8						T,S
Cistothorus platensis. Sedge Wren		33	8		8		95			P/T,N
Thryothorus genibarbis. Moustached Wren	33	33	8	8	8					A,U
Thryothorus leucotis. Buff-breasted Wren	66									A
Thryothorus guarayanus. Fawn-breasted Wren	33	8	95	8	50					L
Troglodytes aedon. House Wren	33	8	8	8	8	8	8		8	W
Troglodytes solstitialis. Mountain Wren			8	8	8	8	8			S,T
Henicorhina leucophrys. Gray-breasted Wood-Wren			8	8	8					S,U
Microcerculus marginatus. Nightingale Wren	89	33	8	8	95					A
Cyphorhinus aradus. Musician Wren	89	33	39	8	95					A
Donacobius atricapillus.(37)										
Black-capped Donacobius	33	8	59	8	50					L

	Pando	Beni	La Paz	Cochabamba	Santa Cruz	Chuquisaca	Tarija	Oruro	Potosí	life zone

CINCLIDAE (dippers; 2 species)

	Pando	Beni	La Paz	Cochabamba	Santa Cruz	Chuquisaca	Tarija	Oruro	Potosí	life zone
Cinclus leucocephalus. White-capped Dipper			8	8	8					H,P/T
Cinclus schulzi. Rufous-throated Dipper							92			U

SYLVIINAE (Old World warblers and gnatcatchers; 2 species)

	Pando	Beni	La Paz	Cochabamba	Santa Cruz	Chuquisaca	Tarija	Oruro	Potosí	life zone
Ramphocaenus melanurus. Long-billed Gnatwren	89‡		103		2a					A
Polioptila dumicola. Masked Gnatcatcher		8		8	8	8	8			N,V

TURDINAE (thrushes; 19 species)

	Pando	Beni	La Paz	Cochabamba	Santa Cruz	Chuquisaca	Tarija	Oruro	Potosí	life zone
Myadestes ralloides. Andean Solitaire			59	8						S,U
Entomodestes leucotis. White-eared Solitaire			8	8						U,S
Catharus fuscater. Slaty-backed Nightingale-Thrush			59	62						S
Catharus dryas. Spotted Nightingale-Thrush			8	8	8	8	8			U
Catharus fuscescens. Veery (N)			92	90						L,V
Catharus ustulatus. Swainson's Thrush (N)		33	8	95	8	8	8			W
Platycichla leucops. Pale-eyed Thrush			8	95	8					U
Turdus chiguanco. Chiguanco Thrush			8	8	8	8	8	8	8	V,P/T
Turdus fuscater. Great Thrush			8	8						P/T,T
Turdus serranus. Glossy-black Thrush			104	8	95		8			H
Turdus nigriceps. Slaty Thrush		100	86	8	8	8	8			U,F
Turdus rufiventris. Rufous-bellied Thrush					8	8	8			N,V
Turdus leucomelas. Pale-breasted Thrush			7		92					N
Turdus amaurochalinus. Creamy-bellied Thrush	33	8	8	8	8	8	8			L,V
Turdus ignobilis. Black-billed Thrush	33	33		95	95					A
Turdus lawrencii. Lawrence's Thrush	66‡		65a*							A
Turdus hauxwelli. Hauxwell's Thrush	33	33	87	8	95					A
Turdus haplochrous. Unicolored Thrush		63			118					N
Turdus albicollis. White-necked Thrush	89	1	8	95	8	8	98			U,A

MIMIDAE (mockingbirds; 3 species)

	Pando	Beni	La Paz	Cochabamba	Santa Cruz	Chuquisaca	Tarija	Oruro	Potosí	life zone
Mimus saturninus. Chalk-browed Mockingbird		8			8	50	8			N
Mimus triurus. White-banded Mockingbird		85*		8	8	50	8			N
Mimus dorsalis. Brown-backed Mockingbird			8	8		22	8	8	8	V

CORVIDAE (jays; 5 species)

	Pando	Beni	La Paz	Cochabamba	Santa Cruz	Chuquisaca	Tarija	Oruro	Potosí	life zone
Cyanolyca viridicyana. Collared Jay			8	8						T,S
Cyanocorax cyanomelas. Purplish Jay		8	8	8	8	8	8			N
Cyanocorax violaceus. Violaceous Jay	66									A
Cyanocorax chrysops. Plush-crested Jay		8		8	8	33	8			N,V
Cyanocorax yncas. Green Jay			8	8						U

VIREONIDAE (vireos; 11 species)

	Pando	Beni	La Paz	Cochabamba	Santa Cruz	Chuquisaca	Tarija	Oruro	Potosí	life zone
Cyclarhis gujanensis. Rufous-browed Peppershrike	33	33	8	8	8	8	8			L,V
Vireolanius leucotis. Slaty-capped Shrikevireo	89	100	8	8	40					U,A
Vireo olivaceus. Red-eyed Vireo	33	33	8	8	8	95	8			L,V
Vireo flavoviridis.(38) Yellow-green Vireo (N)		33		152	152					A
Vireo leucophrys.(39) Brown-capped Vireo			8	8	8					U

	Pando	Beni	La Paz	Cochabamba	Santa Cruz	Chuquisaca	Tarija	Oruro	Potosí	life zone
Hylophilus poicilotis. Rufous-crowned Greenlet		62								N
Hylophilus thoracicus. Lemon-chested Greenlet	33	33	8							A
Hylophilus semicinereus. Gray-chested Greenlet					2a					A
Hylophilus pectoralis. Ashy-headed Greenlet	33									A
Hylophilus hypoxanthus. Dusky-capped Greenlet	33	8	8	8						A
Hylophilus ochraceiceps. Tawny-crowned Greenlet	89	100	8	8	153					A
MOTACILLIDAE (pipits; 5 species)										
Anthus furcatus. Short-billed Pipit			161	22			8	8	8	P
Anthus lutescens. Yellowish Pipit	89	33		161	95	95*	8			L
Anthus correndera. Correndera Pipit			95	95					8	P
Anthus hellmayri. Hellmayr's Pipit			28	8	8	8	8			V
Anthus bogotensis. Paramo Pipit			8	8						P
EMBERIZINAE (40) (emberizines; 64 species)										
Zonotrichia capensis. Rufous-collared Sparrow			8	8	8	8	8	8	8	W
Ammodramus humeralis. Grassland Sparrow		8	95		8	50	8			N
Ammodramus aurifrons. Yellow-browed Sparrow	33	33	8	8	113					A
Phrygilus punensis.(41)										
Olive-backed Sierra-Finch			8							P/T,P
Phrygilus atriceps. Black-hooded Sierra-Finch			8	8		43		8	8	P/T,P
Phrygilus fruticeti. Mourning Sierra-Finch			8	8		95		8	8	V
Phrygilus unicolor. Plumbeous Sierra-Finch			8	8		8		8	8	P
Phrygilus dorsalis. Red-backed Sierra-Finch									8	P
Phrygilus erythronotus. White-throated Sierra-Finch								8	8	P
Phrygilus plebejus. Ash-breasted Sierra-Finch			8	8		95	95	59	8	P
Phrygilus alaudinus. Band-tailed Sierra-Finch			43	8		8	95	8	8	P,V
Haplospiza rustica. Slaty Finch			43	8	95					T,S
Lophospingus pusillus. Black-crested Finch					43		8			N
Lophospingus griseocristatus. Gray-crested Finch			104	8	8	8	95			V
Donacospiza albifrons. Long-tailed Reed-Finch		100								N
Diuca speculifera. White-winged Diuca-Finch			8	8						P
Diuca diuca. Common Diuca-Finch									95	P
Idiopsar brachyurus. Short-tailed Finch			8	88						P
Poospiza boliviana. Bolivian Warbling-Finch			95	43		8	8			V
Poospiza hypochondria.										
Rufous-sided Warbling-Finch			8	8	43	8	8		8	V,P/T
Poospiza erythrophrys.										
Rusty-browed Warbling-Finch				32	95	8	8			V,T
Poospiza nigrorufa.										
Black-and-rufous Warbling-Finch			8	95	8	8	8			V
Poospiza garleppi. Cochabamba Mountain-Finch			8							P/T
Poospiza torquata. Ringed Warbling-Finch			43	8	8	8	8			V
Poospiza melanoleuca. Black-capped Warbling-Finch				8	8	8	8			V,L
Sicalis citrina. Stripe-tailed Yellow-Finch			28							V,P
Sicalis lutea. Puna Yellow-Finch			163					8	8	P
Sicalis uropygialis. Bright-rumped Yellow-Finch			8	8				8	8	P

	Pando	Beni	La Paz	Cochabamba	Santa Cruz	Chuquisaca	Tarija	Oruro	Potosí	life zone
Sicalis luteocephala. Citron-headed Yellow-Finch				8	22	22			8	V
Sicalis olivascens. Greenish Yellow-Finch			8	8		95	52	8	8	V,P
Sicalis flaveola. Saffron Finch		33	59	8	8	8	8			N,V
Sicalis luteola. Grassland Yellow-Finch			104	95	8		50			N,V
Emberizoides herbicola. Wedge-tailed Grass-Finch		8	8		8					N,V
Embernagra platensis. Great Pampa-Finch		33	43	8	95	8	8			N,V,P/T
Volatinia jacarina. Blue-black Grassquit	89	33	8	95	50	8	26			L
Sporophila schistacea. Slate-colored Seedeater	89	56		8	2a					A
Sporophila plumbea. Plumbeous Seedeater	33	33			104					N
Sporophila collaris. Rusty-collared Seedeater		8			104					N
Sporophila lineola. Lined Seedeater	89*	62			54		98			L
Sporophila luctuosa. Black-and-white Seedeater			8	8	8					F,U
Sporophila caerulescens. Double-collared Seedeater	33	8	8	43	95		98			L,V
Sporophila leucoptera. White-bellied Seedeater		8			50					L
Sporophila nigrorufa. Black-and-tawny Seedeater					43					N
Sporophila minuta. Ruddy-breasted Seedeater		84*		95	50					N
Sporophila ruficollis. Dark-throated Seedeater		33			50		26			N
Sporophila castaneiventris. Chestnut-bellied Seedeater	89*	33	8	8						A
Sporophila hypochroma. Rufous-rumped Seedeater		33			8					N
Oryzoborus maximiliani. Greater Large-billed Seedfinch		8			19a					A
Oryzoborus angolensis. Lesser Seedfinch	89	8	86	95	104					A
Catamenia analis. Band-tailed Seedeater			8	8	8	8	8		8	V,P/T
Catamenia inornata. Plain-colored Seedeater			8	8				8		P
Catamenia homochroa. Paramo Seedeater			43	8						P/T
Tiaris obscura.(42) Dull-colored Grassquit			8		43	95	54			N,V,U
Arremon taciturnus. Pectoral Sparrow	33	33	8	8	95					A
Arremon flavirostris. Saffron-billed Sparrow			59	8	8	8	8			N,V
Atlapetes rufinucha. Rufous-naped Brush-Finch			8	8	8					H,P/T
Atlapetes fulviceps. Fulvous-headed Brush-Finch			104	22	43	8	95			H,V,P/T
Atlapetes torquatus. Stripe-headed Brush-Finch			8	8	8	8	8			H
Coryphaspiza melanotis. Black-masked Finch		33								N
Saltatricula multicolor. Many-colored Chaco-Finch					95	95	8			N
Coryphospingus cucullatus. Red-crested Finch		62	8	8	8	95	8			N,V
Paroaria coronata. Red-crested Cardinal		33			50	95	8			N
Paroaria gularis. Red-capped Cardinal	33	33	65a*	8	8					A
Paroaria capitata. Yellow-billed Cardinal					95		8			N
CARDINALINAE (saltators; 12 species)										
Pheucticus aureoventris. Black-backed Grosbeak	33			8	8	50	8		8	H,V
Caryothraustes humeralis.(43) Yellow-shouldered Grosbeak	89		103	90*						A
Pitylus grossus. Slate-colored Grosbeak	33		8							A
Saltator maximus. Buff-throated Saltator	33	33	8	8	95					A,U
Saltator similis. Green-winged Saltator					50					N

	Pando	Beni	La Paz	Cochabamba	Santa Cruz	Chuquisaca	Tarija	Oruro	Potosi	life zone
Saltator coerulescens. Grayish Saltator	33	33	8	95	8		8			L
Saltator aurantiirostris. Golden-billed Saltator			8	8	8	8	8		8	V,P/T
Saltator atricollis. Black-throated Saltator					8					N
Saltator rufiventris. Rufous-bellied Saltator			36	8						P/T
Cyanocompsa cyanoides. Blue-black Grosbeak	33	1	8	8	95					A,U
Cyanocompsa brissonii.(44) Ultramarine Grosbeak			59	8	8	8	8			V,N
Porphyrospiza caerulescens. Blue Finch							50			N

CATAMBLYRHYNCHINAE (plush-capped finches; 1 species)

	Pando	Beni	La Paz	Cochabamba	Santa Cruz	Chuquisaca	Tarija	Oruro	Potosi	life zone
Catamblyrhynchus diadema. Plush-capped Finch			8	8	95					T,S

THRAUPINAE (tanagers; 89 species)

	Pando	Beni	La Paz	Cochabamba	Santa Cruz	Chuquisaca	Tarija	Oruro	Potosi	life zone
Schistochlamys melanopis. Black-faced Tanager	89	8	59		50					L
Neothraupis fasciata. White-banded Tanager					8					N
Cypsnagra hirundinacea. White-rumped Tanager		33			22					N
Lamprospiza melanoleuca. Red-billed Pied Tanager	89	33								A
Cissopis leveriana. Magpie Tanager	33	33	86	8	101*					A,U
Chlorornis riefferii. Grass-green Tanager			8	8						S
Chlorospingus ophthalmicus. Common Bush-Tanager			8	8	8	8	8			S,U
Chlorospingus parvirostris. Short-billed Bush-Tanager			155							S
Hemispingus calophrys.(45) Orange-browed Hemispingus			8	8						T
Hemispingus superciliaris. Superciliaried Hemispingus			59							T
Hemispingus melanotis. Black-eared Hemispingus			8	8	95					U
Hemispingus xanthophthalmus. Drab Hemispingus			103							T
Hemispingus trifasciatus. Three-striped Hemispingus			8	8						T
Thlypopsis sordida. Orange-headed Tanager	33	8	87	8	8	95	8			L
Thlypopsis ruficeps. Rust-and-yellow Tanager			8	8	8	8	95			H,P/T
Hemithraupis guira. Guira Tanager	33	33	8	8	50		8			L
Hemithraupis flavicollis. Yellow-backed Tanager	89	33	104	85*	2a					A
Nemosia pileata. Hooded Tanager	33	8		8	50	60*	8			L
Chlorothraupis carmioli. Carmiol's Tanager		100	8	8						U
Eucometis penicillata. Gray-headed Tanager	33	8		8	62					L
Lanio versicolor. White-winged Shrike-Tanager	33	33	8	8						A
Creurgops dentata. Slaty Tanager			8	59						S
Tachyphonus cristatus. Flame-crested Tanager	33	33			2a					A
Tachyphonus rufiventer. Yellow-crested Tanager		100	8							F,U
Tachyphonus luctuosus. White-shouldered Tanager	33	33	86*	8	50					A
Tachyphonus rufus. White-lined Tanager					92					N
Trichothraupis melanops. Black-goggled Tanager			86	8	8	95				U
Habia rubica. Red-crowned Ant-Tanager	33	33	8	8	8					A
Piranga flava. Hepatic Tanager			8	8	8	8	8			L,U,V
Piranga rubra. Summer Tanager (N)			41	85*						A,V

	Pando	Beni	La Paz	Cochabamba	Santa Cruz	Chuquisaca	Tarija	Oruro	Potosí	life zone
Piranga olivacea. Scarlet Tanager (N)		33	104							U,F
Piranga leucoptera. White-winged Tanager			41	8	95					U
Ramphocelus carbo. Silver-beaked Tanager	33	8	8	8	8					A,U
Ramphocelus nigrogularis.										
Masked Crimson Tanager	66‡									A
Thraupis episcopus. Blue-gray Tanager	89	8	8							A
Thraupis sayaca. Sayaca Tanager		33	8	8	8	8	8			N,V
Thraupis palmarum. Palm Tanager	33	33	8	8	8					A
Thraupis cyanocephala. Blue-capped Tanager			8	8						H
Thraupis bonariensis. Blue-and-yellow Tanager			8	8	8	8	8		8	V
Buthraupis montana. Hooded Mountain-Tanager			8	8						T
Anisognathus igniventris.										
Scarlet-bellied Mountain-Tanager			8	8	95					T
Anisognathus flavinuchus.										
Blue-winged Mountain-Tanager			8	8	8					S,U
Iridosornis jelskii. Golden-collared Tanager			8							T
Delothraupis castaneoventris.										
Chestnut-bellied Mountain-Tanager			8	8	82					T,S
Pipraeidea melanonota. Fawn-breasted Tanager	89	100	8	59	95	95	8			U,V,F
Euphonia chlorotica. Purple-throated Euphonia	89*	8	104	8	8	8	8			V,L
Euphonia laniirostris. Thick-billed Euphonia	33	8	8	8	22					A
Euphonia musica. Blue-hooded Euphonia		8	59	95	8	8	8			V
Euphonia chrysopasta. Golden-bellied Euphonia	33		8	8	50					A
Euphonia mesochrysa. Bronze-green Euphonia			8	8	95					U,F
Euphonia minuta. White-vented Euphonia	33	33	8	41	95					A
Euphonia xanthogaster. Orange-bellied Euphonia	89		8	8						U,A
Euphonia rufiventris. Rufous-bellied Euphonia	33	33	87	95	109					A
Chlorophonia cyanea. Blue-naped Chlorophonia		100	59	8	50					U
Chlorochrysa calliparaea. Orange-eared Tanager			86	8						U
Tangara mexicana. Turquoise Tanager	33	33	8	8	50					A
Tangara chilensis. Paradise Tanager	33	33	8	8	8					A
Tangara schrankii. Green-and-gold Tanager		33	8	8	95					A
Tangara arthus. Golden Tanager			104	8						U
Tangara xanthocephala. Saffron-crowned Tanager			8	8	95					U,S
Tangara chrysotis. Golden-eared Tanager			82	8						U
Tangara xanthogastra. Yellow-bellied Tanager	89		8	90*						A,U
Tangara punctata. Spotted Tanager			8	8						U
Tangara gyrola. Bay-headed Tanager		100	8	8	95					F,U
Tangara cayana. Burnished-buff Tanager		33								N
Tangara ruficervix. Golden-naped Tanager			104	8						S,U
Tangara cyanotis. Blue-browed Tanager			8	59						U
Tangara cyanicollis. Blue-necked Tanager			8	8						F,U
Tangara nigrocincta. Masked Tanager	33	33	104	90*	95					A
Tangara nigroviridis. Beryl-spangled Tanager			86	8						U
Tangara vassorii. Blue-and-black Tanager			8	8	95					H

	Pando	Beni	La Paz	Cochabamba	Santa Cruz	Chuquisaca	Tarija	Oruro	Potosí	life zone
Tangara argyrofenges. Green-throated Tanager			104	8	8					S
Tangara velia. Opal-rumped Tanager	66	90								A
Tangara callophrys. Opal-crowned Tanager	66									A
Dacnis lineata. Black-faced Dacnis	33	33	8	8	2a					A
Dacnis flaviventer. Yellow-bellied Dacnis	89*		86*	35	95					A
Dacnis cayana. Blue Dacnis	33	8	59	8	8					A
Chlorophanes spiza. Green Honeycreeper	33	33	8	8	50					A,U
Cyanerpes caeruleus. Purple Honeycreeper	89	33	59	8	50					A,U
Cyanerpes cyaneus. Red-legged Honeycreeper	33	8			104					A
Oreomanes fraseri. Giant Conebill			8	134					8	P/T
Diglossa baritula. Slaty Flowerpiercer			8	8	8	8	8			V,P/T
Diglossa mystacalis.(46) Moustached Flowerpiercer			8	95						P/T,T
Diglossa carbonaria. Carbonated Flowerpiercer			8	8	95 (135)					P/T,T,V
Diglossa glauca. Deep-blue Flowerpiercer			104	8						U
Diglossa caerulescens. Bluish Flowerpiercer			59							U
Diglossa cyanea. Masked Flowerpiercer			8	8	95					T,S
Tersina viridis. Swallow-Tanager	33	8	8	68*	8					A
Coereba flaveola.(47) Bananaquit		62	8	8	8					F,U
PARULIDAE (wood-warblers; 24 species)										
Parula pitiayumi. Tropical Parula		33	8	8	8	8	8			N,U,V
Dendroica petechia. Yellow Warbler (N)		90*								A
Dendroica cerulea. Cerulean Warbler (N)		33	104							U,F?
Dendroica fusca. Blackburnian Warbler (N)		67*								S
Geothlypis aequinoctialis. Masked Yellowthroat		8	8	8	8	8	8			N,V
Myioborus miniatus. Slate-throated Redstart		100	8	8	95	156				U
Myioborus brunniceps. Brown-capped Redstart			104	36	8	8	8			V,U
Myioborus melanocephalus. Spectacled Redstart			8	8	95					T,S
Basileuterus bivittata. Two-banded Warbler		100	8	8	8	8	8			U
Basileuterus flaveolus. Flavescent Warbler		84*			62					N
Basileuterus luteoviridis. Citrine Warbler			8	8						T,S
Basileuterus signatus. Pale-legged Warbler			8	8	8		95			T,S
Basileuterus coronatus. Russet-crowned Warbler			8	8						U,S
Basileuterus culicivorus. Golden-crowned Warbler		8		8	109					F,N
Basileuterus hypoleucus.(48) White-bellied Warbler					92					N
Basileuterus tristriatus. Three-striped Warbler			8	8	8					U,S
Phaeothlypis fulvicauda. Buff-rumped Warbler	66									A
Phaeothlypis rivularis. River Warbler		8	8	8	117					F
Granatellus pelzelni. Rose-breasted Chat	33	1			2a‡					A
Conirostrum speciosum. Chestnut-vented Conebill	89*	33		59	35	154	8			L
Conirostrum cinereum. Cinereous Conebill			8	8						V,P/T
Conirostrum ferrugineiventre. White-browed Conebill			8	8	95					P/T
Conirostrum sitticolor. Blue-backed Conebill			8	8	68*					T
Conirostrum albifrons. Capped Conebill			8	8	8					S

ICTERIDAE (blackbirds; 26 species)

	Pando	Beni	La Paz	Cochabamba	Santa Cruz	Chuquisaca	Tarija	Oruro	Potosí	life zone
Psarocolius decumanus. Crested Oropendola	33	8	8	8	8	8	8			L
Psarocolius atrovirens. Dusky-green Oropendola			8	8	95					U,S
Psarocolius angustifrons. Russet-backed Oropendola	89*	33	8	8	112					A
Psarocolius bifasciatus.(49) Amazonian Oropendola	33	33	86‡	8	50					A
Cacicus cela. Yellow-rumped Cacique	33	33	8	8	8					A,U
Cacicus haemorrhous. Red-rumped Cacique	89*	71			71					A
Cacicus chrysopterus. Golden-winged Cacique					8	8	95			N
Cacicus leucoramphus.(50) Mountain Cacique			59	8						T,S
Cacicus solitarius. Solitary Black Cacique	89*	33	87	104	50		8			L
Cacicus holosericeus. Yellow-billed Cacique			83	42						T,S
Icterus cayanensis. Epaulet Oriole	33	8	8	8	8	95	8			L,U
Icterus icterus. Troupial	89*	8			8	95				L
Agelaius thilius. Yellow-winged Blackbird			59	42				8		P
Agelaius cyanopus. Unicolored Blackbird		8			70					N
Agelaius ruficapillus. Chestnut-capped Blackbird					50	95	50			N
Leistes militaris.(51) Red-breasted Blackbird	66									A
Leistes superciliaris. White-browed Blackbird		33	33	8	8		8			N
Amblyramphus holosericeus. Scarlet-headed Blackbird		8			95					N
Gnorimopsar chopi. Chopi Blackbird		8			50		50			N
Oreopsar bolivianus. Bolivian Blackbird				8		134			134	V
Lampropsar tanagrinus. Velvet-fronted Grackle		33			91					A
Molothrus badius. Bay-winged Cowbird		33	104	8	95	95	8		8	V,N
Molothrus rufoaxillaris. Screaming Cowbird					95		98			N
Molothrus bonariensis. Shiny Cowbird		33		22	8	8	8		8	L,V
Scaphidura oryzivora. Giant Cowbird	89	8	95*	8	50		60*			L
Dolichonyx oryzivorus. Bobolink (N)	33	1	59	33	95					L

CARDUELIDAE (siskins; 6 species)

	Pando	Beni	La Paz	Cochabamba	Santa Cruz	Chuquisaca	Tarija	Oruro	Potosí	life zone
Carduelis crassirostris. Thick-billed Siskin								100	8	P/T
Carduelis magellanica. Hooded Siskin			115	8	8	8	8	8	8	V
Carduelis olivacea. Olivaceous Siskin			8	8						H
Carduelis xanthogastra. Yellow-bellied Siskin			8	95	8					V,P/T
Carduelis atrata. Black Siskin			8	115			60*	8	8	P/T,P
Carduelis uropygialis. Yellow-rumped Siskin			95						8	P

Introduced Species

COLUMBIDAE (pigeons; 1 species)

	Pando	Beni	La Paz	Cochabamba	Santa Cruz	Chuquisaca	Tarija	Oruro	Potosí	life zone
Columba livia. Rock Dove	89*		94*		94*		60*			W

PLOCEIDAE (weaver-finches; 1 species)

	Pando	Beni	La Paz	Cochabamba	Santa Cruz	Chuquisaca	Tarija	Oruro	Potosí	life zone
Passer domesticus. House Sparrow		25*	105*	95	95	25*	8	25*	8	N,V

| total number of species = 1274 | 490 | 624 | 917 | 802 | 855 | 293 | 379 | 113 | 128 | |

TAXONOMIC FOOTNOTES

1. For reasons for use of *brasilianus* instead of *olivaceus*, see Browning (1989).

2. The taxon *gilvicollis*, formerly thought to be a subspecies of *ruficollis*, is a valid species widely sympatric with the latter (Schwartz 1972).

3. We follow the taxonomy of Strahl (in press) for the Cracidae.

4. See Feldså (1982) for reasons for treatment of *F. ardesiaca* as a valid species rather than a subspecies of *F. americana*.

5. Ingels, Parkes, and Farrand (1981) found that this form, the "Caninde Macaw," formerly treated as a color phase or subspecies of *A. ararauna*, is a valid species known with certainty only from Bolivia.

6. A new species of parakeet, most likely referable to *Nannopsittaca*, that was first collected in Peru in 1987 was seen in 1988 along the Río Heath in Bolivia (Parker, MS).

7. The name *julieni* may be the oldest name for this species (Banks 1988).

8. Although Morony, Bock, and Farrand (1975) followed Peters (1940) in the populations of *Otus ingens* as a separate species nearest *O. albigularis*, Bond (1951) and Traylor (1952) pointed out that *minimus* is a barely recognizable subspecies of *O. ingens*. Fitzpatrick and O'Neill (1986) concluded that "*minimus*" . . . [is] based upon individual variants . . . "

9. See Schulenberg, Allen, Stotz, and Wiedenfeld (1984) for reasons for treating *N. maculosus* as a species distinct from *N. leucopterus*.

10. The highland form *rufiventris*, the only form definitely recorded in Bolivia, is likely a separate species; the sight record from Dpto. Pando, however, is almost certainly of nominate *semitorquatus*.

11. We know of no published evidence supporting the merger by Peters (1940) followed by Morony, Bock, and Farrand (1975), of *C. egregia* with *C. cinereiventris*; in fact, we are unaware of published evidence that the two are even sister taxa (Parker and Remsen 1987); we prefer to follow Meyer de Schauensee (1966, 1970) and retain *egregia* as a full species.

12. Recent treatments, e.g., Morony, Bock, and Farrand (1975), follow Wetmore's (1968: 448) opinion that the tawny-breasted forms should be considered a separate species, *B. martii*, from the green-breasted form, *B. ruficapillus* of eastern South America.

13. See Haffer (1974) for reasons for treating *G. purusianus* as a species distinct from *G. leucotis*.

14. Parker and Remsen (1986) proposed that the populations currently treated as a single species, *Galbula leucogastra*, consist of two valid species, *G. chalcothorax* of western Amazonia and *G. leucogastra* of eastern Amazonia; the Bolivian specimens are *G. leucogastra*.

15. See Haffer (1974) for reasons for treating the taxon *mariae* as a subspecies of *P. flavirostris*.

16. See Haffer (1974) for reasons for treating the taxon *culminatus* as a subspecies of *R. vitellinus*.

17. See Haffer (1974) for reasons for treating the taxon *cuvieri* (and *inca*) as a subspecies of *R. tucanus*.

18. See Short (1982) for reasons for treating the taxon *fuscus* as a full species. Details for the Bolivian records are as follows (L. Short, *in litt.*): three specimens (Amer. Mus. Nat. Hist. ## 791898-900) collected by J. Cuello at Frente a Costa Marguez, Río Itenez, Dpto. Beni, 30 Aug. - 4 Sept. 1964.

19. Short (1982) merged the taxon *dorbignianus*, treated as a full species by previous authors, with *P. cirratus*.

20. We follow Meyer de Schauensee's (1970) classification of the Furnariidae rather than Vaurie's (1980) more recent revision. The changes proposed in Vaurie's monograph are nearly universally unacceptable to those who know the furnariids in the field (e.g., see Remsen 1981, Fitzpatrick 1982, Braun and Parker 1985, and Remsen, Schmitt, and Schmitt, in press).

21. The taxon *superciliosa*, formerly treated as a species, intergrades with *azarae* in Dpto. Cochabamba and should be treated as a subspecies of the latter (Remsen, Schmitt, and Schmitt, in press).

22. See Remsen (1981) and Braun and Parker (1985) for reasons for not following Vaurie's recommendation to merge all *Schizoeaca* into one species.

23. This species is perhaps best treated as a large, high elevation subspecies of the highly variable *A. dorbignyi*.

24. The highland and lowland forms of this species should perhaps be treated as members of separate species complexes. The highland form (*ochrogaster*) is ochraceous ventrally, whereas the lowland form (*lyra*) is buffy-white.

25. This species, formerly considered a subspecies of *C. lineatus*, occurs sympatrically with the latter and differs strongly in plumage and vocalizations (Pierpont and Fitzpatrick 1983).

26. An undescribed species of *Cercomacra* has been collected at Balta and other localities in southeastern Peru, primarily in bamboo thickets; the technical description is in progress (J. Fitzpatrick, *in litt.*). See Parker and Remsen (1987) for notes on its natural history in Bolivia.

27. Lanyon (1984, 1985, 1986) is undertaking a generic revision of the Tyrannidae, which to date has covered the Tyrannine, Myiarchine, and *Empidonax* groups. In the course of this work, he has named several new genera and has shifted the relationships of many others. Although we find his work convincing, we do not want to use a "hybrid"

54

classification in our checklist, and so we retain the order and sequence of "Peters" (Traylor 1979). Lanyon's new genera are noted in our footnotes.

28. The taxon *munda* is usually treated as a separate species from *S. subcristata*. Recent information on vocalizations (Remsen, pers. obs.; recordings deposited at Florida State Museum) supports the traditional treatment. The song of *munda* is a soft, spitting, syncopated "tsi, tsu-tsu, tsu-tsu, tsu-tsu," and thus differs dramatically from the song of *subcristata*, which is a soft trill preceded by an inflected introductory note: "sweee?, titititititi."

29. Recent biochemical and morphological data (Zink and Johnson 1984; Lanyon and Lanyon 1986) indicate that this species, formerly considered a member of the genus *Empidonax*, is more closely related to the genera *Aphanotriccus* and *Cnemotriccus*.

30. Recent data on the morphology of the syrinx and nasal capsule indicate that this species not only is not a member of the genus *Ochthoeca* but is probably not even a member of the "*Ochthoeca* group" of genera (Lanyon 1986).

31. All Bolivian records are of the southern taxa *pallidior* and *bellicosa*, which together almost certainly deserve recognition as a species distinct from *sclateri* of the Andes from Peru to Venezuela (along with *ferruginea* of the tepui region). The southern taxa differ strongly from the northern ones in plumage pattern and coloration.

32. Lanyon (1984) summarized evidence that this species is so different from *P. sulphuratus* that it warrants recognition of a separate new genus, *Philohydor*.

33. Lanyon (1984) summarized evidence that this species is so different from *E. varius* that it warrants recognition of a separate new genus, *Griseotyrannus*.

34. See Remsen, Parker, and Ridgely (1982) for reasons for merging *Chirocylla* into *Lipaugus*.

35. Parker and Remsen (1987) presented reasons for treating the taxon *boliviana* of the foothills of northern Bolivia and southern Peru as a species distinct from *C. pareola*.

36. See Stiles (1981) for reasons for treating *ruficollis* as a species distinct from *S. serripennis* of North America.

37. *Donacobius*, formerly placed in the Mimidae, is a member of the Troglodytidae (M. H. Clench, J. L. Gulledge, and K. C. Parkes, unpubl. data; AOU 1983).

38. Johnson and Zink (1985) presented biochemical data that favor treatment of this species as a separate species from *V. olivaceus*. No specimen of North American *V. o. olivaceus* has been recorded in Bolivia.

39. We follow the AOU (1983) in treating the Neotropical populations of the *V. gilvus* complex as a separate species from *V. leucophrys*; recent biochemical data (Johnson, Zink, and Marten 1988) support this treatment.

40. Recent evidence from DNA-DNA hybridization studies (Bledsoe 1988) indicates that many South American "emberizines" (e.g., *Sicalis*, *Diuca*) are more closely related to tanagers than they are to other emberizines.

41. Paynter's (1970) revision of the *Phrygilus gayi* group considered all Bolivian populations to be representatives of *P. atriceps*, although no justification has been published. We here follow the taxonomy used by Vuilleumier (1982), who recognized as a distinct species (*chloronotus*) the gray-headed populations that occur north of *atriceps*. We use Hellmayr's (1938: 345) English name "Olive-backed" for this species; although the subspecies occurring in Bolivia, *punensis*, is not as olive-backed as populations to the north, the difference is slight.

42. See Clark (1986) for a summary of evidence for placing this species, previously considered a member of the genus *Sporophila*, in the genus *Tiaris*.

43. It is highly unlikely that *humeralis* belongs in the genus *Caryothraustes*. The species *humeralis* differs strongly in its general behavior from other *Caryothraustes*: it is a rather quiet bird found in pairs within mixed-species flocks of canopy birds (vs. noisy, gregarious, and not normally found in mixed-species flocks as in other *Caryothraustes* spp.). Hellmayr (1938), who also felt that this species did not belong in *Caryothraustes*, pointed out the differences in bill structure and plumage between *humeralis* and the other *Caryothraustes* species.

44. See Eisenmann (1979) for reasons for suppression of *cyanea*, the former specific name for this taxon.

45. See Weske and Terborgh (1974) for reasons for treating this form as a species separate from *H. atropileus*.

46. We follow Vuilleumier (1969b) in treating the southern forms of the *D. lafresnayii* superspecies as a full species, *D. mystacalis*.

47. Bledsoe (1988) found (using DNA-DNA hybridization) that *Coereba* is more closely related to tanagers than to warblers.

48. Presence of varying amounts of yellow in the underparts of individuals of this species in Mato Grosso (Hellmayr 1935: 497) and the Cerro Santiago area of Dpto. Santa Cruz (Remsen, unpubl. data, LSUMZ specimens) may indicate local introgression with *B. culicivorus*. In Brazil, mixed pairs have been seen, but the two taxa generally differ in habitat preferences (Willis 1986). Although the close relationship between *B. hypoleucus* and *B. culicivorus* has long been recognized (Hellmayr 1935, Meyer de Schauensee 1970), Lowery and Monroe's (1968) linear sequence of the Parulidae, adopted by Morony, Bock, and Farrand (1975), placed five other species between these two, with no explanation given.

49. See Haffer (1974) for reasons for treating *P. yuracares* as a subspecies of *P. bifasciatus*.

50. The taxon *chrysonotus* was treated as a species distinct from *C. leucoramphus* by Blake (1968).

51. For reasons presented in Parker and Remsen (1987), we do not follow Short's (1968) recommended merger of *Leistes* into *Sturnella*; Orians (1985) also maintained *Leistes* as a genus.

HYPOTHETICAL LIST

Eudromia elegans. Elegant Crested-Tinamou. A chick that is probably of this species has been collected in Bolivia (Banks 1977), but addition to the main list awaits confirmation of the identification (Remsen and Traylor 1983).

Buteo albigula. White-throated Hawk. T. A. Parker and J. V. Remsen saw what was almost certainly this species near Chuspipata, Dpto. La Paz (Remsen 1985). Bruce D. Glick (pers. comm.) and Rose Ann Rowlett saw one in the same general area on 7 November 1985. In view of the difficulties in identification of South American buteos, we prefer to wait for specimen confirmation before addition to the main list.

Crax ?estudilloi. This species is known from one aviary bird (which recently died and has been deposited as a specimen, through the efforts of J. Estudillo Lopez and S. D. Strahl, at the Louisiana State University Museum of Natural Science) obtained as a captive chick in Dpto. La Paz, Bolivia (Estudillo Lopez 1977). Although a number of cracid experts feel that this bird represents a valid species, we remain cautious until a thorough analysis of the specimen is completed; therefore, we follow Vuilleumier and Mayr (1987) in listing this as a "species inquirenda" because: (a) no detailed description or analysis of its relationships has been published; (b) Vuilleumier noticed that the individual in question resembled another bird of known hybrid origin in the same aviary; and (c) only one specimen is known. Furthermore, we note that because the bird was raised in captivity, the possibility needs to be addressed that its unique character, its light green base of the bill, is not merely the consequence of inappropriate diet or other developmental abnormalities. We also note that aberrancies in the plumage of cracids seem to occur with abnormally high frequency (Teixeira and Sick 1986); perhaps such variation extends to soft part colors as well.

Laterallus viridis. Russet-crowned Crake. Niethammer (1953) published a sight record of this species from Dpto. La Paz. Although the details of his sighting are suggestive, nothing is mentioned concerning the field marks of the bird. We prefer to wait for better documentation before addition to the main list.

Charadrius alexandrinus. Snowy Plover. Chubb (1919) reported that three specimens of this species were collected by Perry O. Simons at Challapata, 3700 m (Dpto. Oruro). Although this is the only report of this coastal species from the Andes, its authenticity has never been questioned: this record was included by Bond and Meyer de Schauensee (1943) in their list of the birds of Bolivia and in all subsequent reference works. We asked Dr. P. R. Colston to check Simons' specimens at the British Museum to see if they were not C. [*falklandicus*] *alticola*, a common altiplano plover similar in appearance to C. *alexandrinus*; Colston (in litt.) found that the specimens were indeed C. [*falklandicus*] *alticola*.

Catoptrophorus semipalmatus. Willet. This species was listed from "Bolivia" without comment by Forbes and Robinson (1899) and has been included in the list of Bolivian birds by several subsequent authors. In view of the indefinite nature of the record and Bolivia's shifting political boundaries, we do not feel that this coastal species should be added to the main list. We are unable to locate any inland records of this species from South America.

Gallinago undulata. Giant Snipe. This species was listed by Olrog (1968) and Meyer de Schauensee (1970) for Bolivia. Although this species will almost certainly be found to occur in Bolivia, we are unable to find a published locality record or unpublished specimen for the country.

Larus cirrocephalus. Gray-hooded Gull. This species was listed for Bolivia by Meyer de Schauensee (1966, 1970) and by Olrog (1968) on the basis of a statement (Hornero 6: 361: "llegando a las costas del Peru por Bolivia") that this species crosses the Bolivian Andes to reach the Peruvian coast. Although this may be true, no valid record for Bolivia exists. Furthermore, recent discovery of breeding colonies on the Pacific coast of South America by Tovar and Ashmole (1970) and Ridgely and Wilcove (1979) provides an alternative explanation for the origin of birds on the Peruvian coast.

Pyrrhura devillei. Blaze-winged Parakeet. Although the type locality for this species is "Bolivia," the type was described in 1854, and so the precise locality may very well have been in that portion of the country subsequently lost to Paraguay in the Chaco War. No specimens have been collected from a locality definitely within the modern boundaries of Bolivia. Furthermore, *P. molinae*, a presumed allospecies of *P. devillei*, occurs in extreme southeastern Dpto. Santa Cruz and adjacent Mato Grosso (Darrieu 1980); overlap between the two would seem unlikely. Fjeldså (1987) reported a questionable sight record from the Andes of extreme southern Dpto. Cochabamba.

Nandayus nenday. Black-hooded Parakeet. Orfila (1937) listed this species as having been recorded in Bolivia at "Bahia Blanca" but did not state the basis for this record. Bolivia has been included in the range of this species on the basis of Orfila's report by many subsequent authors. However, we have been unable to locate a specimen or the locality. "Bahia Blanca" may be a mistake for Bahia Negra, where Grant (1911) collected this species. Bahia Negra was formerly in Bolivia but is now part of Paraguay. This species does occur near the Bolivian border in Mato Grosso, Brazil, near Corumba' (T. A. Parker III, pers. comm.).

Brotogeris chrysopterus. Golden-winged Parakeet. Friedmann (1945a) included in his analysis a specimen from "Bolivia" without comment. Richard C. Banks (in litt.) examined the specimen (U.S. National Museum #306558) and found that the bird is correctly identified to species (and labelled as the subspecies *B. c. chrysosema*); the specimen, however, was originally an aviary bird, with an abnormally long and hooked upper mandible, that arrived at the National Zoological Park (#2991) on 26 June 1926 with the locality of origin given as "Rurrenabaque, Rio Beni, Bolivia." This locality is at the extreme western edge of the Amazonian lowlands of Bolivia, a highly unlikely locality for *B. chrysopterus*, a Brazilian species expected to occur in Bolivia, if at all, in extreme eastern dptos. Beni or Pando. The western section of Dpto. Beni is occupied by an allospecies of *B. chrysopterus*, *B. cyanoptera*; in fact, the latter has been collected at El Consuelo, only 30 km east of Rurrenabaque (Gyldenstolpe 1945). Although strong seasonal movements of *B. chrysopterus* (as yet unknown) cannot be ruled out as an explanation for such apparent overlap, in view of the suspicious circumstances of the Rurrenabaque record, the conservative view is that if the specimen did indeed originate from Rurrenabaque, it was first transported there by parrot dealers and then exported from there.

Haffer (1987) included extreme northeastern Bolivia in the range of *B. chrysopterus* because he considered the subspecies *beniensis*, currently considered a subspecies of *B. cyanoptera*, to be a subspecies of *B. chrysopterus*. If *B. chrysopterus* occurs in Bolivia, it would probably be most likely to be found in the area of extreme northeastern Dpto. Santa Cruz where several species previously not known from east of the Madeira-Guaporé drainage have been found recently (Bates *et al.*, in press).

Crotophaga sulcirostris. Groove-billed Ani. Johnson (1967), Olrog (1968), and Dunning (1982) included Bolivia in the range of this species. We can find no valid record for Bolivia.

Asio stygius. Stygian Owl. Olrog (1968) included Bolivia in the range of this species, but we are unable to locate any specimens or published locality records. Fjeldså (1987) reported a sight record by Neils Krabbe from Parque Nacional Tunari, Dpto. Cochabamba.

Chordeiles minor. Common Nighthawk. Pearson (1975b) and Dott (1985) reported sight records of this species from dptos. Beni and Chuquisaca. Because of the difficulty of distinguishing this species from *C. acutipennis* in the field, we feel that addition to the main list should be confirmed by a specimen or recordings of vocalizations.

Heliodoxa branickii. Rufous-webbed Brilliant. This species was listed for Bolivia by Bond and Meyer de Schauensee (1943) on the basis of a skin seen on a tribal artifact in a museum in La Paz; most authors have included Bolivia in the range of this species on this basis. Not only is the origin of the skin uncertain, but the identification of the specimen has not been confirmed.

Coeligena iris. Rainbow Starfrontlet. This species was included by Bond and Meyer de Schauensee (1943) in their list of the bird species of Bolivia (as *Diphogena aurora*). Zimmer (1951a) discussed the reasons for regarding as erroneous earlier records from Bolivia for this species, which is not known south of central Peru (Meyer de Schauensee 1966).

Metallura phoebe. Black Metaltail. This species was listed for Bolivia by Bond and Meyer de Schauensee (1943) and Olrog (1968), and with a question-mark by Meyer de Schauensee

(1966, 1970). There is no specimen known from the modern boundaries of Bolivia.

Eulidia yarrellii. Chilean Woodstar. This species was included by Bond and Meyer de Schauensee (1943) in their list of the birds of Bolivia and noted as "recorded from western Bolivia." According to Hellmayr (1932), Delattre collected it at Cobija, "Bolivia" (now Chile), and the "Bolivia" has persisted in the literature. Gyldenstolpe's (1945) record from El Consuelo, Dpto. Beni, based on a provisionally identified juvenal male, is essentially impossible. *E. yarrellii* is known only from the Pacific lowlands of extreme southern Peru and northern Chile (Parker 1982).

Monasa atra. Black Nunbird. Meyer de Schauensee and Phelps (1978) included Bolivia in the range of this species. There is no record of this species in Bolivia, which is occupied by the closely related *M. nigrifrons*; perhaps Meyer de Schauensee and Phelps considered them conspecific.

Celeus flavescens. Blond-crested Woodpecker. This species was listed for Bolivia by Meyer de Schauensee (1966, 1970) and Olrog (1968), but Short (1972) found no evidence for its occurrence in Bolivia, where its allospecies, *C. lugubris*, is found throughout the southeastern sector of the country.

Drymornis bridgesi. Scimitar-billed Woodcreeper. This species was listed for "southeastern Bolivia" by Short (1975) and for Tarija by Meyer de Schauensee (1982: 449). We have been unable to locate a specimen to support this.

Premnornis guttuligera. Rusty-winged Barbtail. Remsen and Ridgely (1980) reported Ridgely's sight record from Dpto. Cochabamba. Although the observer is reliable and experienced with this species, which has been collected within a few kilometers of the Bolivian border in Dpto. Puno, Peru (LSUMZ specimens), we prefer to wait for confirmation of this species in Bolivia.

Thamnomanes caesius. Cinereous Antshrike. Meyer de Schauensee and Phelps (1978) and Dunning (1982) included Bolivia in the range of this species. Taxonomic confusion with *T. schistogynus*, considered by some a subspecies of *T. caesius*, may be the source of Bolivian records of the latter (as was the case for Pearson's (1975) attributing Bolivian records of *T. caesius* to Gyldenstolpe's (1945) records of *T. (c.) schistogynus*). Although *T. caesius* may occur in extreme east-central Bolivia (Table 1), we are unable to find a specimen from Bolivia.

Grallaria andicola. Stripe-headed Antpitta. A mounted specimen of this species in the Museo Nacional de Historia Natural, La Paz, probably came from Bolivia, but the specimen has no label. Dunning (1982) included Bolivia in the range of this species without providing details. J. Fjeldså (in litt.) heard and glimpsed one individual in appropriate habitat in the upper Zongo Valley, Dpto. La Paz, on 10 April 1987.

Todirostrum nigriceps. Black-headed Tody-Flycatcher. Meyer de Schauensee and Phelps (1978) listed this species as occurring in Bolivia; they seem to have confused this taxon with *T. chrysocrotaphum*, the related form that occurs in Bolivia.

Conioptilon mcilhennyi. Black-faced Cotinga. In June 1986 near Porvenir, Dpto. Pando, T. A. Parker (pers. comm.) heard a *Turdus hauxwelli* that gave perfect imitations in its playback-response song of the call note of this rare cotinga. Although *Conioptilon mcilhennyi* occurs within 280 km of Bolivia (Table 1) and although we strongly suspect that this presumably nonmigratory thrush learned its imitation locally, we cannot rule out the possibility of cultural transmission of such an imitated vocalization through the thrush's range.

Sporophila nigricollis. Yellow-bellied Seedeater. This species was listed by Meyer de Schauensee (1966) for "Bolivia in Santa Cruz," and several subsequent authors have included Bolivia in the range of this species. We are unable to find a citation or unpublished specimen for Bolivia.

Xanthopsar flavus. Saffron-cowled Blackbird. This species was listed for Bolivia by Meyer de Schauensee (1970). We are unable to find a citation or unpublished specimen for Bolivia.

Olrog (1968) included Bolivia in the distribution statement or range map of several species for which we are unable to find a specimen, published locality record, or previously published reference in the literature. Although many of these are likely to occur in Bolivia, we prefer to wait for a definite record before inclusion on the main list; his inclusion of other species in the list of Bolivian birds is clearly erroneous (e.g., *Capito hypoleucus*, *Pteroglossus f. flavirostris*). The species are: *Nothura maculosa*, *Eudromia formosa*, *Anas discolor*, *Anas sibilatrix*, *Netta erythrophthalma*, *Milvago chimango*, *Larus (ridibundus) maculipennis*, *Scardafella squammata*, *Bolborhynchus lineola*, *Forpus passerinus*, and *Trogon rufus*.

Dunning's (1982) range maps of South American birds included at least 21 species for which we can find no valid record: *Chaetura chapmani*, *Phlogophilus harterti*, *Polytmus theresiae*, *Trogon rufus*, *Galbula albirostris*, *Monasa flavirostris*, *Upucerthia albigula*, *Leptasthenura striata*, *Synallaxis ruficapilla*, *S. cherrei*, *Anumbius annumbi*, *Xenops milleri*, *Frederickena unduligera*, *Thamnophilus cryptoleucus*, *Myrmotherula schisticolor*, *M. iheringi*, *Conopophaga peruviana*, *Myiobius barbatus*, *Neopipo cinnamomea*, *Pipra pipra*, and *Chlorospingus flavigularis*. Although many or most of these will probably be found eventually in Bolivia (Table 1), we can find no valid records of any of these species. Dunning's maps also included Bolivia in the range of about 15 other species for which there was no valid record at the time but which have recently been found in the country (e.g., Parker and Remsen 1987, Bates *et al.*, in press).

A recent book on Bolivian birds ("Aves de Bolivia," by Noel Kempff Mercado, 1985, Editorial Gisbert, La Paz) listed at least 62 species for which no valid record for Bolivia has been published: *Podiceps major*, *Egretta caerulea*, *Botaurus pinnatus*, *Anas sibilatrix*, *A. discors*, *Netta erythrophthalma*, *Buteo albigula*, *Milvago chimango*, *Falco columbarius*, *Larus maculipennis*, *Scardafella squammata*, *Bolborhynchus lineola*, *Forpus passerinus*, *Brotogeris chrysopterus*, *Crotophaga sulcirostris*, *Asio stygius*, *Chaetura chapmani*, *Lophornis magnifica*, *Polytmus theresiae*, *Phlogophilus harterti*, *Trogon rufus*, *Baryphthengus ruficapillus*, *Galbula albirostris*, *Nonnula rubecula*, *Monasa flavirostris*, *M. atra*, *Capito hypoleucus*, *C. aurovirens*, *Drymornis bridgesi*, *Upucerthia albigula*, *Anumbius annumbi*, *Leptasthenura striata*, *Synallaxis albigularis*, *Synallaxis cherriei*, *S. moesta*, *S. ruficapilla*, *Xenops milleri*, *Frederickena unduligera*, *Thamnophilus cryptoleucus*, *Thamnomanes caesius*, *Myrmotherula schisticolor*, *M. iheringi*, *Grallaria andicola*, *Conopophaga peruviana*, *Liosceles thoracicus*, *Pachyramphus rufus*, *Conioptilon mcilhennyi*, *Pipra erythrocephala*, *P. pipra*, *Neopipo cinnamomea*, *Knipolegus orenocensis*, *Empidonax traillii*, *Todirostrum nigriceps*, *Microbates cinereiventris*, *Vireo altiloquus*, *Oryzoborus crassirostris*, *Cyanerpes nitidus*, *Dendroica striata*, *Basileuterus nigrocristatus*, *Psarocolius oseryi*, *P. viridis*, and *Gymnomystax mexicanus*. Many of these species were included by Kempff because of their incorrect listing by previous authors of field guides and popular books, especially Olrog (1968) and Dunning (1982); these species are dealt with directly in the species accounts above. Other species listed by Kempff are listed because of taxonomic changes or controversies in recent literature to which Kempff understandably did not have access (e.g., *Baryphthengus ruficapillus*, *Synallaxis moesta*, *Todirostrum nigriceps*, *Empidonax traillii*, *Pachyramphus rufus*, *Pipra erythrocephala*, *Oryzoborus crassirostris*, *Basileuterus nigrocristatus*). In addition to the 62 species above, Kempff also included in his list 22 species found by Parker and Remsen (1987) in 1986 or Bates *et al.* (in press) in 1988 that were the first valid records for Bolivia, although Dunning (1982) or Olrog (1968) included Bolivia in the range of many of these 22 species without justification. For the remainder of the 62 species, Kempff provided no specific documentation. Many of the species occur near Bolivia and may eventually be found within the country (see Table 1); some of these might have been recorded by Kempff, but the details were not published before his unfortunate and untimely death. Users of Kempff's list should also beware of numerous errors in nomenclature and life zone designations.

LITERATURE CITED

(1) ALLEN, J. A. 1889. List of the birds collected in Bolivia by Dr. H. H. Rusby, with field notes by the collector. Bull. Amer. Mus. Nat. Hist. 2: 77-112.

AMERICAN ORNITHOLOGISTS' UNION. 1983. Check-list of North American birds, 6th edition. Amer. Ornith. Union, Lawrence, Kansas.

(2) BANGS, O. & T. PENARD. 1921. Notes on some American birds, chiefly Neotropical. Bull. Mus. Comp. Zool. 64: 364-394.

BANKS, R. C. 1977. A review of the crested tinamous (Aves: Tinamidae). Proc. Biol. Soc. Wash. 89: 529-544.

BANKS, R. C. 1988. An old record of the Pearly-breasted Cuckoo in North America and a nomenclatural critique. Bull. Brit. Ornith. Club 108: 87-91.

(2a) BATES, J. M., M. C. GARVIN, C. G. SCHMITT, & D. S. SCHMITT. Notes on bird distribution in the Parque Nacional Noel Kempff Mercado, extreme northeastern Dpto. Santa Cruz, Bolivia. Bull. Brit. Ornith. Club (in press).

(3) BERLEPSCH, H. G. von. 1907. Descriptions of new species and conspecies of Neotropical birds. Ornis 14 (= Proc. 4th Intern. Ornith. Congr.): 347-371.

BLAKE, E. R. 1968. Family Icteridae. Pp. 138-202 in "Check-list of birds of the world, Vol. XIV" (Paynter, R. A., Jr., ed.). Museum of Comparative Zoology, Cambridge, Mass.

BLEDSOE, A. H. 1988. Nuclear DNA evolution and phylogeny of the New World nine-primaried oscines. Auk 105: 504-515.

(4) BOND, J. 1945. Notes on Peruvian Furnariidae. Proc. Acad. Nat. Sci. Philadelphia. 97: 17-39.

(5) BOND, J. 1947. Notes on Peruvian Tyrannidae. Proc. Acad. Nat. Sci. Philadelphia 99: 127-154.

(6) BOND, J. 1950. Notes on Peruvian Formicariidae. Proc. Acad. Nat. Sci. Philadelphia 102: 1-26.

BOND, J. 1951. Taxonomic notes on South American birds. Auk 68: 527-529.

(7) BOND, J. 1956. Additional notes on Peruvian birds, II. Proc. Acad. Nat. Sci. Philadelphia 108: 227-247.

(8) BOND, J. & R. MEYER DE SCHAUENSEE. 1942. The birds of Bolivia. Part I. Proc. Acad. Nat. Sci. Philadelphia 94: 307-391.

(9) BOND, J. & R. MEYER DE SCHAUENSEE. 1943. The birds of Bolivia. Part II. Proc. Acad. Nat. Sci. Philadelphia 95: 167-221.

BRAUN, M. J. & T. A. PARKER, III. 1985. Molecular, morphological, and behavioral evidence concerning the taxonomic relationships of "Synallaxis" gularis and other synallaxines. Pp. 333-346 in "Neotropical ornithology" (P. A. Buckley et al., eds.), Ornithol. Monogr. No. 36.

(10) BRIDGES, T. 1847. Notes in addition to former (Zool. Proc. 1843, p. 108, and 1846, p. 9) papers on South American ornithology. Proc. Zool. Soc. London 1847: 28-30.

BROWNING, M. R. 1989. The correct name for the Olivaceus Cormorant, "Maiagua" of Piso (1658). Wilson Bull. 101: 101-106.

(11) CABOT, J. 1986. Falco peregrinus cassini en Bolivia. Doñana, Acta Vertebrata 13: 183-186.

(12) CABOT, J., J. CASTROVIEJO, & V. URIOS. Cuatro nuevas especies de aves para Bolivia. Doñana, Acta Vertebrata (submitted).

(13) CABOT, J. & P. SERRANO. 1986. Data on the distribution of some species of raptors in Bolivia. Bull. Brit. Ornith. Club 106: 170-172.

(13a) CABOT, J. & P. SERRANO. 1988. Distributional data on some non-passerine species in Bolivia. Bull. Brit. Ornith. Club 108: 187-193.

(14) CARDIFF, S. W. & J. V. REMSEN, JR. 1981. Three bird species new to Bolivia. Bull. Brit. Ornith. Club 101: 304-305.

(15) CHAPMAN, F. M. 1928. Mutation in *Capito auratus*. Amer. Mus. Novit. No. 335.

(16) CHUBB, C. 1919. Notes on collections of birds in the British Museum, from Ecuador, Peru, Bolivia, and Argentina. Ibis: 1-55, 256-290.

CLARK, G. A., JR. 1986. Systematic interpretations of foot-scute patterns in Neotropical finches. Wilson Bull. 98: 594-597.

(16a) CLARKE, R. O. S. Amboro National Park bird list. The first 500. (in press MS).

(17) CORY, C. B. & C. E. HELLMAYR. 1924. Catalogue of birds of the Americas. Field Mus. Nat. Hist., Zool. Ser. 13, pt. 3, 369 pp.

(18) CORY, C. B. & C. E. HELLMAYR. 1925. Catalogue of birds of the Americas. Field Mus. Nat. Hist., Zool. Ser. 13, pt. 4, 390 pp.

(18a) COX, G. & R. O. CLARKE. 1988. Erste Ergebnisse einer Studie über den Bolivianischen Helmhokko *Pauxi unicornis* in Amboró-Nationalpark, Bolivien. Trochilus 9:96-101.

(19) DARRIEU, C. A. 1979. *Aratinga aurea*, distribucion en America del Sur y variaciones subespecificas (Aves, Psittacidae). Neotropica 25: 119-126.

DARRIEU, C. A. 1980. Las razas geograficas de *Pyrrhura molinae* (Aves, Psittacidae). Rev. Mus. Argentino Cienc. Natur. "Bernardino Rivadavia" 12: 161-176.

(19a) DAVIS, S. E. MS. Birds of Concepción, Dpto. Santa Cruz, Bolivia. Unpublished manuscript (specimens deposited at FMNH).

(20) DAVIS, T. J. & J. P. O'NEILL. 1986. A new species of antwren (*Herpsilochmus*: Formicariidae) from northern Peru, with comments on the sytematics of other members of the genus. Wilson Bull. 98: 337-352.

(21) DONAHUE, P. K. 1986. Sight record of Red Knot for Bolivia. Amer. Birds 40: 224.

(22) D'ORBIGNY, A. D. 1847. Voyage dans l'Amerique Meridionale. Vol. 4, pt. 3, Oiseaux. P. Bertrand, Paris, 395 pp.

(23) DOTT, H. E. M. 1984. Range extensions, one new record, and notes on winter breeding of birds in Bolivia. Bull. Brit. Ornith. Club 104: 104-109.

(24) DOTT, H. E. M. 1985. North American migrants in Bolivia. Condor 87: 343-345.

(25) DOTT, H. E. M. 1986. The spread of the House Sparrow *Passer domesticus* in Bolivia. Ibis 128: 132-137.

DUNNING, J. S. 1982. South American land birds. Harrowood Books, Newton Square, Pennsylvania.

EISENMANN, E. 1979. Specific name of the Indigo Bunting conserved. Auk 96: 766.

(26) EISENTRAUT, A. 1935. Biologische Studien im bolivianischen Chaco. VI. Beitr. zur Biologie der Vogelfauna. Mitt. Zool. Mus. Berlin 20: 367-443.

ESTUDILLO LOPEZ, J. 1977. New species of curassow discovered. Game Bird Breeders Avicult. Zoo. Conserv. Gaz. 26: 6-7.

FITZPATRICK, J. 1982. [Review of]: Taxonomy and geographical distribution of the Furnariidae (Aves, Passeriformes), by Charles Vaurie. Auk 99: 810-813.

FITZPATRICK, J. W. & J. P. O'NEILL. 1986. *Otus petersoni*, a new screech-owl from the eastern Andes, with systematic notes on *O. columbianus* and *O. injens*. Wilson Bull. 98: 1-14.

FJELDSÅ, J. 1982. Biology and systematic relationships of the Andean coot "*Fulica americana ardesiaca*" (Aves, Rallidae). Steenstrupia 8: 1-21.

FJELDSÅ, J. 1985. Origin, evolution, and status of the avifauna of Andean wetlands. Pp. 85-112 in "Neotropical ornithology" (P. A. Buckley *et al.*, eds.). Ornithol. Monogr. No. 36.

FJELDSÅ, J. 1987. Birds of relict forests in the high Andes of Peru and Bolivia. Zoological Museum, University of Copenhagen, Denmark.

(27) FJELDSÅ, J. & N. KRABBE. 1986. Some range extensions and other unusual records of Andean birds. Bull. Brit. Ornith. Club 106: 115-124.

(28) FJELDSÅ, J. & N. KRABBE. An unpublished major avian collection from the Bolivian highlands. MS submitted to Folia Scripta.

(28a) FJELDSÅ, J., N. KRABBE, & T. A. PARKER, III. 1987. Rediscovery of *Cinclodes excelsior aricomae* and notes on the nominate race. Bull. Brit. Ornith. Club 107: 129-134.

FORBES, H. O. & H. C. ROBINSON. 1899. Catalogue of the Charadriomorphic birds (Charadriformes[sic]) in the Derby Museum. Bull. Liverpool Mus. 2: 51-75.

(29) FRIEDMANN, H. 1935. A new race of the crested eagle-hawk, *Spizaetus ornatus*. J. Wash. Acad. Sci. 25: 450-451.

FRIEDMANN, H. 1945a. Two new birds from the upper Rio Negro, Brazil. Proc. Biol. Soc. Wash. 58: 113-116.

(30) FRIEDMANN, H. 1945b. *Cypseloides major* in Bolivia. Auk 62: 460.

(31) FRIEDMANN, H. 1950. Birds of North and Middle America, pt. XI. Bull. U. S. Nat. Mus. 50, pt. 11, 793 pp.

GRANT, C. H. B. 1911. List of birds collected in Argentina, Paraguay, Bolivia, and southern Brazil, with field-notes. Part II. Picariae-Anatidae. Ibis: 317-350.

(32) GYLDENSTOLPE, N. 1941. Preliminary diagnoses of some new birds from Bolivia. Arkiv Zool., Band 33B, No. 13.

(33) GYLDENSTOLPE, N. 1945. A contribution to the ornithology of northern Bolivia. Kungl. Svenska Vet.-Akad. Handl., ser. 3, 23(1), 300 pp.

GYLDENSTOLPE, N. 1951. The ornithology of the Rio Purús region in western Brazil. Arkiv Zoologi (Ser. 2) 2: 1-320.

HAFFER, J. 1974. Avian speciation in tropical South America. Publ. Nuttall Ornith. Club No. 14.

HAFFER, J. 1987. Biogeography of Neotropical birds. Pp. 105-150 in "Biogeography and Quaternary history in tropical America" (T. C. Whitmore & G. T. Prance, eds.), Clarendon Press, Oxford.

(34) HELLMAYR, C. E. 1917. Beschreibung von sechs neuen neotropischen Vogel formen, nebst einer Bermerkung uber *Ampelion cinctus* (Tsch.). Verh. Orn. Ges. Bayern 13: 106-119.

(35) HELLMAYR, C. E. 1921. Review of the birds collected by Alcide d'Orbigny in South America. Parts I and II. Novit. Zool. 28: 171-213; 230-276.

(36) HELLMAYR, C. E. 1925. Review of the birds collected by Alcide d'Orbigny in South America, pts. 4-6. Novit. Zool. 32: 1-30, 175-194, 314-334.

(37) HELLMAYR, C. E. 1927. Catalogue of birds of the Americas. Field Mus. Nat. Hist., Zool. Ser. 13, pt. 5, 517 pp.

(38) HELLMAYR, C. E. 1929. Catalogue of birds of the Americas. Field Mus. Nat. Hist., Zool. Ser. 13, pt. 6, 258 pp.

HELLMAYR, C. E. 1932. The birds of Chile. Field Mus. Nat. Hist., Zool. Ser. 19, 472 pp.

(39) HELLMAYR, C. E. 1934. Catalogue of birds of the Americas. Field Mus. Nat. Hist., Zool. Ser. 13, pt. 7, 531 pp.

(40) HELLMAYR, C. E. 1935. Catalogue of birds of the Americas. Field Mus. Nat. Hist., Zool. Ser. 13, pt. 8, 541 pp.

(41) HELLMAYR, C. E. 1936. Catalogue of birds of the Americas. Field Mus. Nat. Hist., Zool. Ser. 13, pt. 9, 458 pp.

(42) HELLMAYR, C. E. 1937. Catalogue of birds of the Americas. Field Mus. Nat. Hist., Zool. Ser. 13, pt. 10, 228 pp.

(43) HELLMAYR, C. E. 1938. Catalogue of birds of the Americas. Field Mus. Nat. Hist., Zool. Ser. 13, pt. 11, 662 pp.

(44) HELLMAYR, C. E. & B. CONOVER. 1942. Catalogue of birds of the Americas. Field Mus. Nat. Hist., Zool. Ser. 13, pt. 1, no. 1, 636 pp.

(45) HELLMAYR, C. E. & B. CONOVER. 1948a. Catalogue of birds of the Americas. Field Mus. Nat. Hist., Zool. Ser. 13, pt. 1, No. 2, 434 pp.

(46) HELLMAYR, C. E. & B. CONOVER. 1948b. Catalogue of birds of the Americas. Field Mus. Nat. Hist., Zool. Ser. 13, pt. 1, No. 3, 383 pp.

(47) HELLMAYR, C. E. 1949. Catalogue of birds of the Americas. Field Mus. Nat. Hist., Zool. Ser. 13, pt. 1, No. 4., 358 pp.

HOWELL, T. R., R. A. PAYNTER, JR., & A. L. RAND. 1968. Subfamily Carduelinae. Pp. 207-306 in "Checklist of birds of the world, Vol. XIV" (R. A. Paynter, Jr., ed.). Museum of Comparative Zoology, Cambridge, Mass.

(48) INGELS, J., K. C. PARKES, & J. FARRAND, JR. 1981. The status of the macaw generally but incorrectly called *Ara caninde* (Wagler). Gerfaut 71: 283-294

JOHNSON, A. W. 1967. The birds of Chile and adjacent regions of Argentina, Bolivia and Peru. Vol. 2. Platt Establecimientos Gráficos, Buenos Aires.

JOHNSON, N. K. & R. M. ZINK. 1985. Genetic evidence for relationships among the Red-eyed, Yellow-green, and Chivi vireos. Wilson Bull. 97: 421-435.

JOHNSON, N. K., R. M. ZINK, & J. A. MARTEN. 1988. Genetic evidence for relationships in the avian family Vireonidae. Condor 90: 428-445.

(49) LANYON, W. E. 1978. Revision of the *Myiarchus* flycatchers of South America. Bull. Amer. Mus. Nat. Hist. 161: 427-627.

LANYON, W. E. 1984. A phylogeny of the kingbirds and their allies. Amer. Mus. Novit. 2797.

LANYON, W. E. 1985. A phylogeny of the Myiarchine flycatchers. Pp. 361-382 in "Neotropical Ornithology" (Buckley, P. A. et al., eds.). Ornithol. Monogr. No. 36.

LANYON, W. E. 1986. A phylogeny of the thirty-three genera in the *Empidonax* assemblage of tyrant flycatchers. Amer. Mus. Novit. 2846.

LANYON, W. E. & S. M. LANYON. 1986. Generic status of Euler's Flycatcher: a morphological and biochemical study. Auk 103: 341-350.

(50) LAUBMANN, A. 1930. Vogel. Wissenschaftliche Ergebnisse der Deutschen Gran Chaco-Expedition. Strecker and Schroder, Stuttgart, 334 pp.

(51) LAUBMANN, A. 1934. Weitere Beitrage zur Avifauna Argentiniens. Verh. Orn. Ges. Bayern 20: 249-336.

(52) LÖNNBERG, E. 1903. On a collection of birds from northwestern Argentina and the Bolivian Chaco. Ibis: 441-471.

LOWERY, G. H., Jr. & B. L. MONROE, Jr. 1968. Family Parulidae. Pp. 3-93 in "Check-list of birds of the world, Vol. XIV" (Paynter, R. A., Jr., ed.). Museum of Comparative Zoology, Cambridge, Mass.

(53) MENEGAUX, A. 1909. Etude d'une collection d'oiseaux provenant des hauts plateaux de la Bolivie et du Perou meridional. Bull. Soc. Philom Paris, ser. 10, 1: 205-229.

(54) MEYER DE SCHAUENSEE, R. 1952. A review of the genus *Sporophila*. Proc. Acad. Nat. Sci. Philadelphia 104: 153-196.

(55) MEYER DE SCHAUENSEE, R. 1953. Manakins and cotingas from Ecuador and Peru. Proc. Acad. Nat. Sci. Philadelphia 105: 29-43.

(56) MEYER DE SCHAUENSEE, R. 1966. The species of birds of South America with their distribution. Livingston, Narberth, Pennsylvania, 577 pp.

MEYER DE SCHAUENSEE, R. 1970. A guide to the birds of South America. Livingston, Wynnewood, Pennsylvania, 470 pp.

MEYER DE SCHAUENSEE, R. 1982. A guide to the birds of South America. International Council for Bird Preservation, Intercollegiate Press.

MEYER DE SCHAUENSEE, R. & W. H. PHELPS, JR. 1978. A guide to the birds of Venezuela. Princeton Univ. Press.

MORONY, J. J., W. J. BOCK, & J. FARRAND, Jr. 1975. Reference list of birds of the world. Amer. Mus. Nat. Hist., New York.

(57) NEUMANN, O. 1931. Neue Unterarten sudamerikanischer Vogel. Mitt. Zool. Mus. Berlin 17: 441-445.

(58) NIETHAMMER, G. 1953. Zur Vogelwelt Boliviens. Bonn. zool. Beitr. 4: 195-303.

(59) NIETHAMMER, G. 1956. Zur Vogelwelt Boliviens (Teil II: Passeres). Bonn. zool. Beitr. 7: 84-150.

(60) NORES, M. & D. YZURIETA. 1984. Registro de aves en el sur de Bolivia. Acta Vertebrata Doñana 11: 327-337.

(61) OLROG, C. 1949. Notas ornitologicas sobre la coleccion del Instituto Miguel Lillo (Tucumán). Acta Zool. Lilloana 8: 209-217.

(62) OLROG, C. 1963. Notas sobre aves bolivianas. Acta Zool. Lilloana 19: 407-478.

OLROG, C. C. 1968. Las aves sudamericanas. Una guia de campo. Tomo primero. Universidad Nacional de Tucumán.

OLROG, C. & F. CONTINO. 1970. Dos especies nuevas para la avifauna argentina. Neotropica 16: 94-95.

O'NEILL, J. P. 1974. The birds of Balta, a Peruvian dry tropical forest locality, with an analysis of their origins and ecological relationships. Unpubl. dissertation, Louisiana State Univ.

(63) O'NEILL, J. P. 1976. Notes on two species of Bolivian birds. Wilson Bull. 88: 492-493.

(64) O'NEILL, J. P. & A. L. GARDNER. 1974. Rediscovery of *Aulacorhynchus prasinus dimidiatus* (Ridgway). Auk 91: 700-704.

ORFILA, R. N. 1937. Los Psittaciformes argentinos. Hornero 6: 365-380.

ORIANS, G. H. 1985. Blackbirds of the Americas. Univ. Washington, Seattle.

ORIANS, G. H., L. ERCKMANN, & J. C. SCHULTZ. 1977. Nesting and other habits of the Bolivian Blackbird (*Oreopsar bolivianus*). Condor 79: 250-256.

PARKER, T. A. III. 1981. Distribution and biology of the White-cheeked Cotinga *Zaratornis stresemanni*, a high Andean frugivore. Bull. Brit. Ornith. Club 101: 256-265.

PARKER, T. A. III. 1982. First record of the Chilean Woodstar *Eulidia yarrellii* in Peru. Bull. Brit. Ornith. Club 102:86.

(65) PARKER, T. A. III. 1984. Notes on the behavior of *Ramphotrigon* flycatchers. Auk 101: 186-188.

(65a) PARKER, T. A., III. MS. Observations on birds of the Río Heath, Peru and Bolivia.

(66) PARKER, T. A., III, & J. V. REMSEN, JR. 1987. Fifty-two Amazonian bird species new to Bolivia. Bull. Brit. Ornith. Club. 107: 94-106.

(67) PARKER, T. A. III, J. V. REMSEN, JR., & J. A. HEINDEL. 1980. Seven bird species new to Bolivia. Bull. Brit. Ornith. Club 100: 160-162.

(68) PARKER, T. A. III & R. A. ROWLETT. 1984. Some noteworthy records of birds from Bolivia. Bull. Brit. Ornith. Club 104: 110-113.

PARKER, T. A. III, S. A. PARKER, & M. A. PLENGE. 1982. An annotated checklist of Peruvian birds. Buteo Books, Vermillion, South Dakota.

(69) PARKES, K. C. 1960. The Brown Cachalote, *Pseudoseisura lophotes*, in Bolivia. Auk 77: 226-227.

(70) PARKES, K. C. 1966. Geographic variation in Azara's Marsh Blackbird, *Agelaius cyanopus*. Proc. Biol. Soc. Wash. 79: 1-12.

(71) PARKES, K. C. 1970. A revision of the Red-rumped Cacique, *Cacicus haemorrhous* (Aves: Icteridae). Proc. Biol. Soc. Wash. 83: 203-214.

(72) PARKES, K. C. 1973. Distribution and generic placement of the Plain Tyrannulet (*Inezia inornata*). Condor 75: 249-250.

(73) PARKES, K. C., D. P. KIBBE, & E. L. ROTH. 1978. First records of the Spotted Rail (*Pardirallus maculatus*) for the United States, Chile, Bolivia, and western Mexico. Amer. Birds 32: 295-299.

(74) PARTRIDGE, W. H. 1956. Variaciones geográficas en la lechuza negra, *Ciccaba huhula*. Hornero 10: 143-145.

PAYNTER, R. A., Jr. 1970. Subfamily Emberizinae. Pp. 3-214 in "Check-list of birds of the world, Vol. XIII" (Paynter, R. A., Jr., ed.). Museum of Comparative Zoology, Cambridge, Mass.

PAYNTER, R. A., Jr. & M. A. TRAYLOR, JR. 1977. Ornithological gazetteer of Ecuador. Museum of Comparative Zoology, Cambridge, Mass.

PAYNTER, R. A., JR., M. A. TRAYLOR, JR., & B. WINTER. 1975. Ornithological gazetteer of Bolivia. Museum of Comparative Zoology, Cambridge, Mass.

(75) PEARSON, D. L. 1975a. Range extensions and new records for bird species in Ecuador, Peru, and Bolivia. Condor 77: 96-99.

(76) PEARSON, D. L. 1975b. Un estudio de las aves de Tumi Chucua, Departamento Beni, Bolivia. Pumapunku 8: 50-56.

(77) PENA, L. E. 1961. Results of research in the Antofagasta ranges of Chile and Bolivia. I. Birds. Postilla 49: 3-42.

PETERS, J. L. 1940. Check-list of birds of the world. Vol 4. Museum of Comparative Zoology, Cambridge, Mass.

(78) PETERS, J. L. 1951. Check-list of birds of the world. Vol. 7. Museum of Comparative Zoology, Cambridge, Mass.

PIERPONT, N. & J. W. FITZPATRICK. 1983. Specific status and behavior of *Cymbilaimus sanctaemariae*, the Bamboo Antshrike, from southwestern Amazonia. Auk 100: 645-652.

(79) PLENGE, M. A. 1982. The distribution of the Lesser Rhea *Pterocnemia pennata* in southern Peru and northern Chile. Ibis 124: 168-172.

(80) REMSEN, J. V., JR. 1981. A new subspecies of *Schizoeaca harterti* with notes on taxonomy and natural history of *Schizoeaca* (Aves: Furnariidae). Proc. Biol. Soc. Wash. 94: 1068-1075.

(81) REMSEN, J. V., JR. 1984a. Geographic variation, zoogeography, and possible rapid evolution in some *Cranioleuca* spinetails (Furnariidae) of the Andes. Wilson Bull. 96: 515-523.

(82) REMSEN, J. V., JR. 1984b. Natural history notes on some poorly known Bolivian birds, part 2. Gerfaut 74: 163-179.

(83) REMSEN, J. V., JR. 1985. Community organization and ecology of birds of high elevation humid forest of the Bolivian Andes. Pp. 733-756 in "Neotropical ornithology" (Buckley, P. A., *et al.*, eds.). Ornithol. Monogr. No. 36

(84) REMSEN, J. V., JR. 1986. Aves de una localidad en la sabana húmeda del norte de Bolivia. Ecología en Bolivia 8: 21-36.

(85) REMSEN, J. V., JR. New bird records for Dpto. Cochabamba, Bolivia. Comun. Mus. Nac. Hist. Natur. (in press).

(86) REMSEN, J. V., JR. MS. Ecological profile of a lower montane cloud forest in northern Bolivia.

(87) REMSEN, J. V., JR. & S. M. LANYON. MS. Ecological profile of a foothill forest locality in the tropical zone of northern Bolivia.

REMSEN, J. V., JR. & T. A. PARKER, III. 1984. Contribution of river-created habitats to species richness in Amazonia. Biotropica 15: 223-231.

(88) REMSEN, J. V., JR., T. A. PARKER, III, & R. S. RIDGELY. 1982. Natural history notes on some poorly known Bolivian birds. Gerfaut 72: 77-87.

(89) REMSEN, J. V., JR., T. A. PARKER, III, C. E. QUINTELA, & K. V. ROSENBERG. MS. An ecological profile of a tropical forest in Amazonian Bolivia.

(90) REMSEN, J. V., JR. & R. S. RIDGELY. 1980. Additions to the avifauna of Bolivia. Condor 82: 69-75.

(91) REMSEN, J. V., JR., C. G. SCHMITT, & D. C. SCHMITT. Natural history notes on some poorly known Bolivian birds. Part 3. Gerfaut (in press).

(92) REMSEN, J. V., JR. & M. A. TRAYLOR, JR. 1983. Additions to the avifauna of Bolivia, part 2. Condor 85: 95-98.

(93) REMSEN, J. V., JR., M. A, TRAYLOR, JR., & K. C. PARKES. 1985. Range extensions for some Bolivian birds (Tinamiformes to Charadriiformes). Bull. Brit. Ornith. Club 105: 124-130.

(94) REMSEN, J. V., JR., M. A. TRAYLOR, JR., & K. C. PARKES. 1986. Range extensions for some Bolivian birds, 2 (Columbidae to Rhinocryptidae). Bull. Brit. Ornith. Club 106: 22-32.

(95) REMSEN, J. V., Jr., M. A. TRAYLOR, JR., & K. C. PARKES. 1987. Range extensions for some Bolivian birds, 3 (Tyrannidae to Passeridae). Bull. Brit. Ornith. Club 107: 6-16.

RIDGELY, R. S. 1981. The current distribution and status of mainland Neotropical parrots. ICBP Tech. Bull. 1: 233-384.

RIDGELY, R. S. & D. S. WILCOVE. 1979. First nesting record of Gray-hooded Gull from Ecuador. Condor 81: 438-439.

(96) RUSCHI, A. 1967. Beija-flores da região de "San Matias" na Bolivia. Bol. Mus. Biol. Prof. Mello Leitão, Zool. Ser., no. 29, 8 pp.

(97) SALVADORI, T. 1891. Catalogue of the Psittaci, or parrots, in the collection of the British Museum. Cat. Birds Brit. Mus. 20, 658 pp.

(98) SALVADORI, T. 1897. Viaggio del Dott. Alfredo Borelli nel Chaco boliviano e nella Republica Argentina. 7. Uccelli. Boll. Mus. Zool. Anat. Comp. Torino 12 (292): 36 pp.

(99) SCHMITT, C. G. & D. C. COLE. 1981. First records of Black-legged Seriema (*Chunga burmeisteri*) in Bolivia. Condor 83: 182-183.

(100) SCHMITT, C. G. & D. C. SCHMITT. 1987. Extensions of range for some Bolivian birds. Bull. Brit. Ornith. Club 107: 129-134.

(101) SCHMITT, C. G., D. C. SCHMITT, J. V. REMSEN, JR., & B. D. GLICK. 1986. New bird records for Departamento Santa Cruz, Bolivia. Hornero 12: 307-311.

(102) SCHUCHMANN, K.-L. 1984. Two hummingbird species, one a new subspecies, new to Bolivia. Bull. Brit. Ornith. Club 104: 5-7.

SCHULENBERG, T. S., S. E. ALLEN, D. F. STOTZ, & D. A. WIEDENFELD. 1984. Distributional records from the Cordillera Yanachaga, central Peru. Gerfaut 74: 57-70.

SCHULENBERG, T. S. & L. C. BINFORD. 1985. A new species of tanager (Emberizidae: Thraupinae, *Tangara*) from southern Peru. Wilson Bull. 97: 413-420.

(103) SCHULENBERG, T. S. & J. V. REMSEN, JR. 1982. Eleven bird species new to Bolivia. Bull. Brit. Ornith. Club 102: 52-57.

SCHWARTZ, P. 1972. *Micrastur gilvicollis*, a valid species sympatric with *M. ruficollis* in Amazonia. Condor 74: 399-415.

(104) SCLATER, P. L. & O. SALVIN. 1879. On the birds collected in Bolivia by Mr. C. Buckley. Proc. Zool. Soc. London 1879: 588-645.

(105) SERRANO P., P. & J. CABOT N. 1983. *Passer domesticus*, nueva especie para Bolivia. Acta Vertebrata Doñana 10: 212-213.

(106) SHAW, D. & T. C. MAXWELL. 1988. First record of the Mississippi Kite for Bolivia. J. Raptor Res. 22:90.

SHORT, L. L. 1968. Sympatry of red-breasted meadowlarks in Argentina and the taxonomy of meadowlarks (Aves: *Leistes*, *Pezites*, and *Sturnella*). Amer. Mus. Novit. 2349.

(107) SHORT, L. L. 1969. The southern races of the White-throated Spadebill (*Platyrinchus mystaceus*). Auk 86: 265-270.

SHORT, L. L. 1972. Relationships among the four species of the superspecies *Celeus elegans* (Aves, Picidae). Amer. Mus. Novit. No. 2487.

SHORT, L. L. 1975. A zoogeographic analysis of the South American chaco avifauna. Bull. Amer. Mus. Nat. Hist. 154: 165-352.

(108) SHORT, L. L. 1982. Woodpeckers of the world. Delaware Mus. Nat. Hist., Monogr. Ser., No. 4.

SIBLEY, C. G., J. E. AHLQUIST, & B. L. MONROE, JR. 1988. A classification of the living birds of the world based on DNA-DNA hybridization studies. Auk 105: 409-423.

STEPHENS, L. & M. A. TRAYLOR, JR. 1983. Ornithological gazetteer of Peru. Museum of Comparative Zoology, Cambridge, Mass.

STILES, F. G. 1981. The taxonomy of Rough-winged Swallows (*Stelgidopteryx:* Hirundinidae) in southern Central America. Auk 98: 282-293.

STRAHL, S. D. Conservation strategy for the Cracidae. Proc. First International Cracid Symp. (in press]TEIXEIRA, D. M. & H. SICK. 1986. Plumage variation and plumage aberration in Cracidae. Rev. Brasil. Biol. 46: 777-779.

TERBORGH, J. W., J. W. FITZPATRICK, & L. EMMONS. 1984. Annotated checklist of bird and mammal species of Cocha Cashu Biological Station, Manu National Park, Peru. Fieldiana (Zool.) (New Ser.) No. 21.

(109) TODD, W. E. C. 1913. Preliminary diagnoses of apparently new birds from tropical America. Proc. Biol. Soc. Wash. 26: 169-174.

(110) TODD, W. E. C. 1915. Preliminary diagnoses of seven apparently new Neotropical birds. Proc. Biol. Soc. Wash. 28: 169-170.

(111) TODD, W. E. C. 1916. Preliminary diagnoses of fifteen apparently new Neotropical birds. Proc. Biol. Soc. Wash. 29: 95-98.

(112) TODD, W. E. C. 1917. Preliminary diagnoses of apparently new birds from Colombia and Bolivia. Proc. Biol. Soc. Wash. 30: 3-6.

(113) TODD, W. E. C. 1920. Descriptions of apparently new South American birds. Proc. Biol. Soc. Wash. 33: 71-75.

(114) TODD, W. E. C. 1921. Studies in the Tyrannidae. I. A revision of the genus *Pipromorpha.* Proc. Biol. Soc. Wash. 34: 173-192.

(115) TODD, W. E. C. 1926. A study of the neotropical finches of the genus *Spinus.* Ann. Carnegie Mus. 17: 11-82.

(116) TODD, W. E. C. 1927. New gnateaters and antbirds from tropical America with a revision of the genus *Myrmeciza* and its allies. Proc. Biol. Soc. Wash. 40: 149-178.

(117) TODD, W. E. C. 1929. A revision of the wood-warbler genus *Basileuterus.* Proc. U. S. Nat. Mus. 74, Art. 7, 95 pp.

(118) TODD, W. E. C. 1931. Critical notes on Neotropical thrushes. Proc. Biol. Soc. Wash. 44: 47-54.

(119) TODD, W. E. C. 1937. The pigeons of the *Columba plumbea* group. Proc. Biol. Soc. Wash. 50: 185-190.

(120) TODD, W. E. C. 1942a. List of the tinamous in the collection of the Carnegie Museum. Ann. Carnegie Mus. 29: 1-29.

(121) TODD, W. E. C. 1942b. List of the hummingbirds in the collection of the Carnegie Museum. Ann. Carnegie Mus. 29: 271-370.

(122) TODD, W. E. C. 1943a. Critical remarks on the trogons. Proc. Biol. Soc. Wash. 56: 3-15.

(123) TODD, W. E. C. 1943b. Studies in the jacamars and puffbirds. Ann. Carnegie Mus. 30: 1-18.

(124) TODD, W. E. C. 1943c. Critical remarks on the toucans. Proc. Biol. Soc. Wash. 56: 153-162.

(125) TODD, W. E. C. 1946. Critical notes on the woodpeckers. Ann. Carnegie Mus. 30: 297-317.

(126) TODD, W. E. C. 1947. Two new owls from Bolivia. Proc. Biol. Soc. Wash. 60: 95-96.

(127) TODD, W. E. C. 1950. Critical notes on the cotingas. Proc. Biol. Soc. Wash. 63: 5-8.

(128) TODD, W. E. C. 1952. New tyrant flycatchers from South America. Ann. Carnegie Mus. 32: 291-304.

(129) TODD, W. E. C. 1954. A new gallinule from Bolivia. Proc. Biol. Soc. Wash. 67: 85-86.

TOVAR, H. S. & N. P. ASHMOLE. 1970. A breeding record for the Gray-hooded Gull, *Larus cirrocephalus*, on the Peruvian coast. Condor 72: 119-122.

(130) TRAYLOR, M. A., JR. 1951. A review of the woodpeckers *Chrysoptilus melanochloros* and *C. melanolaimus*. Fieldiana (Zool.) 31: 421-437.

TRAYLOR, M. A., JR. 1952. A new race of *Otus ingens* (Salvin) from Colombia. Nat. Hist. Misc., Chicago Acad. Sci. 99: 1-4.

TRAYLOR, M. A., JR. 1979. Family Tyrannidae. Pp. 1-245 in "Check-list of birds of the world, Vol. VIII (Traylor, M. A., ed.). Museum of Comparative Zoology, Cambridge, Mass.

(131) TRAYLOR, M. A., JR. 1982. Notes on tyrant flycatchers (Aves: Tyrannidae). Fieldiana (Zool.) No. 13.

(132) TRAYLOR, M. A., JR. 1985. Species limits in the *Ochthoeca diadema* species-group (Tyrannidae). Pp. 431-442 in "Neotropical ornithology" (Buckley, P. A. *et al.*, eds.). Ornithol. Monogr. No. 36.

(133) VAURIE, C. 1962. A systematic study of the Red-backed Hawks of South America. Condor 64: 277-290.

VAURIE, C. 1980. Taxonomy and geographical distribution of the Furnariidae (Aves, Passeriformes). Bull. Amer. Mus. Nat. Hist. 166: 1-357.

(134) VUILLEUMIER, F. 1969a. Field notes on some birds from the Bolivian Andes. Ibis 111: 599-608.

(135) VUILLEUMIER, F. 1969b. Systematics and evolution in *Diglossa* (Aves, Coerebidae). Amer. Mus. Novit. No. 2381.

VUILLEUMIER, F. 1982. Ecological aspects of speciation in birds, with special reference to South American birds. Pp. 101-148 in "Ecología y genetica de la especiacion animal" (Reig, O. A., ed). Symposia Universidad Simón Bolivar, Primeras Jornadas Scientificas.

VUILLEUMIER, F. & E. MAYR. 1987. New species of birds described from 1976 to 1980. J. Orn. 128: 137-150.

VUILLEUMIER, F. & D. SIMBERLOFF. 1980. Ecology versus history as determinants of patchy and insular distributions in high Andean birds. Evol. Biol. 12: 235-379.

WESKE, J. W. & J. TERBORGH. 1974. *Hemispingus parodii*, a new species of tanager from Peru. Wilson Bull. 86: 97-103.

WETMORE, A. 1968. The birds of the Republic of Panamá. Part 2.--Columbidae (pigeons) to Picidae (woodpeckers). Smithsonian Misc. Coll. 150, pt. 2.

WILLIS, E. O. 1986. Vireos, wood warblers and warblers as ant followers. Gerfaut 76: 177-186.

(136) ZIMMER, J. T. 1931a. Studies of Peruvian birds. I. New and other birds from Peru, Ecuador, and Brazil. Amer. Mus. Novit. 500: 1- 23.

(137) ZIMMER, J. T. 1931b. Studies of Peruvian birds. II. Peruvian forms of the genera *Microbates, Ramphocaenus, Sclateria, Pyriglena, Pithys, Drymophila*, and *Liosceles*. Amer. Mus. Novit. 509: 1-20.

(138) ZIMMER, J. T. 1932a. Studies of Peruvian birds. VI. The formicarian genera *Myrmoborus* and *Myrmeciza* in Peru. Amer. Mus. Novit. 545: 1-24.

(139) ZIMMER, J. T. 1932b. Studies of Peruvian birds. VII. The genera *Pygiptila, Megastictus, Dysithamnus, Thamnomanes, Cercomacra*, and *Phlegopsis*. Amer. Mus. Novit. 558: 1-25.

(140) ZIMMER, J. T. 1933. Studies of Peruvian birds. IX. The formicarian genus *Thamnophilus*. Part 1. Amer. Mus. Novit. 646: 1-22.

(141) ZIMMER, J. T. 1934. Studies of Peruvian birds. XIV. Notes on the genera *Dendrocolaptes, Hylexetastes, Xiphocolaptes, Dendroplex*, and *Lepidocolaptes*. Amer. Mus. Novit. 753: 1-26.

(142) ZIMMER, J. T. 1936. Studies of Peruvian birds. XXIII. Notes on *Doliornis, Pipreola, Attila, Laniocera, Rhytipterna*, and *Lipaugus*. Amer. Mus. Novit. 893: 1-15.

(143) ZIMMER, J. T. 1937a. Studies of Peruvian birds. XXV. Notes on the genera *Thamnophilus, Thamnocharis, Gymnopithys*, and *Ramphocaenus*. Amer. Mus. Novit. 917: 1-16.

(144) ZIMMER, J. T. 1937b. Studies of Peruvian birds. XXVI. Notes on the genera *Agriornis, Muscisaxicola, Myiotheretes, Ochthoeca, Colonia, Knipolegus, Phaeotriccus, Fluvicola*, and *Ramphotrigon*. Amer. Mus. Novit. 930: 1-27.

(145) ZIMMER, J. T. 1937c. Studies of Peruvian birds. XXVII. Notes on the genera *Muscivora, Tyrannus, Empidonomus*, and *Sirystes*, with further notes on *Knipolegus*. Amer. Mus. Novit. 962: 1-28.

(146) ZIMMER, J. T. 1937d. Studies of Peruvian birds. XXVIII. Notes on the genera *Myiodynastes, Conopias, Myiozetetes*, and *Pitangus*. Amer. Mus. Novit. 963: 1-28.

(147) ZIMMER, J. T. 1939a. Studies of Peruvian birds. XXX. Notes on the genera *Contopus, Empidonax, Terenotriccus*, and *Myiobius*. Amer. Mus. Novit. 1042: 1-13.

(148) ZIMMER, J. T. 1939b. Studies of Peruvian birds. XXXII. The genus *Scytalopus*. Amer. Mus. Novit. 1044: 1-18.

(149) ZIMMER, J. T. 1939c. Studies of Peruvian birds. XXXIII. The genera *Tolmomyias* and *Rhynchocyclus* with further notes on *Ramphotrigon*. Amer. Mus. Novit. 1045: 1-23.

(150) ZIMMER, J. T. 1940. Studies of Peruvian birds. XXXIV. The genera *Todirostrum, Euscarthmornis, Snethlagea, Poecilotriccus, Lophotriccus, Myiornis, Pseudotriccus*, and *Hemitriccus*. Amer. Mus. Novit. 1066: 1-23.

(151) ZIMMER, J. T. 1941. Studies of Peruvian birds. XXXVII. The genera *Sublegatus, Phaeomyias, Camptostoma, Xanthomyias, Phyllomyias*, and *Tyranniscus*. Amer. Mus. Novit. 1109: 1-25.

(152) ZIMMER, J. T. 1941b. Studies of Peruvian birds, XXXIX. The genus *Vireo*. Amer. Mus. Novit. 1127: 1-20.

(153) ZIMMER, J. T. 1942a. Studies of Peruvian birds. XLI. The genera *Hylophilus, Smaragdolanius*, and *Cyclarhis*. Amer. Mus. Novit. 1160: 1-16.

(154) ZIMMER, J. T. 1942b. Studies of Peruvian birds. XLIII. Notes on the genera *Dacnis, Xenodacnis, Coereba, Conirostrum*, and *Oreomanes*. Amer. Mus. Novit. 1193: 1-16.

(155) ZIMMER, J. T. 1947. Studies of Peruvian birds. No. 52. The genera *Sericossypha, Chlorospingus, Cnemoscopus, Hemispingus, Conothraupis, Chlorornis, Lamprospiza, Cissopis*, and *Schistochlamys*. Amer. Mus. Novit. 1367: 1-26.

(156) ZIMMER, J. T. 1949. Studies of Peruvian birds. No. 54. The families Catamblyrhynchidae and Parulidae. Amer. Mus. Novit. 1428: 1-59.

(157) ZIMMER, J. T. 1950a. Studies of Peruvian birds. No. 55. The hummingbird genera *Doryfera, Glaucis, Threnetes*, and *Phaethornis*. Amer. Mus. Novit. 1449: 1-51.

(158) ZIMMER, J. T. 1950b. Studies of Peruvian birds. No. 58. The genera *Chlorostilbon, Thalurania, Hylocharis*, and *Chrysuronia*. Amer. Mus. Novit. 1474: 1-31.

(159) ZIMMER, J. T. 1951a. Studies of Peruvian birds. No. 60. The genera *Heliodoxa, Phlogophilus, Urosticte, Polyplancta, Adelomyia, Coeligena, Ensifera, Oreotrochilus*, and *Topaza*. Amer. Mus. Novit. 1513: 1-45.

(160) ZIMMER, J. T. 1951b. Studies of Peruvian birds. No. 61. The genera *Agleactis, Lafresnaya, Pterophanes, Boissonneaua, Heliangelus, Eriocnemis, Haplophaedia, Ocreatus,* and *Lesbia.* Amer. Mus. Novit. 1540: 1-55.

(161) ZIMMER, J. T. 1953. Studies of Peruvian birds. No. 65. The jays (Corvidae) and pipits (Motacillidae). Amer. Mus. Novit. 1649: 1-27.

(162) ZIMMER, J. T. 1955. Studies of Peruvian birds. No. 66. The swallows (Hirundinidae). Amer. Mus. Novit. 1723: 1-35.

ZINK, R. M. & N. K. JOHNSON. 1984. Evolutionary genetics of flycatchers. I. Sibling species in the genera *Empidonax* and *Contopus.* Syst. Zool. 33: 205-216.

(163) UNPUBLISHED SPECIMEN RECORDS:

(1) *Plegadis chihi,* Chuquisaca: El Cabrada, 4300 m (British Museum, fide J. Fjeldså);

(2) *Microstilbon burmeisteri,* La Paz: Tilo Tilo (BM #87.3.22.1147, fide J. Fjeldså);

(3) *Sittasomus griseicapillus,* Chuquisaca: 16 km N Monteagudo, 5000 ft., 28 Nov. 1972; 70 km SE Padilla, 3600 ft., 18 & 23 Nov. 1973, coll. by R. Crossin (Field Mus. Nat. Hist. 293806-7, 293811);

(4) *Myrmotherula assimilis,* Beni: Frente a Costa Marguez, Río Itenez (Amer. Mus. Nat. Hist. #792018; *fide* D. F. Stotz);

(5) *Sicalis lutea,* La Paz: Esperanza, 4200 m, 5-24 Oct. 1941, coll. by F. Steinbach (FMNH 182954-9).

INDEX TO ENGLISH NAMES IN MAIN LIST

INDEX TO GENERA AND FAMILIES IN MAIN LIST